100 LITERACY HOMEWORK

SCHOLASTIC

RENEWED PRIMARY FRAMEWORK

100 LITERACY

HOMEWORK

ACTIVITIES

SCOTTISH PRIMARY 5

YEAR
4

Credits

Author
Chris Webster

Updated by
Pam Dowson

Series consultant
Pam Dowson

Series editor
Tracy Kewley

Development editor
Rachel Mackinnon

Assistant editor
Alex Albrighton

Illustrations
Garry Davies, Phil Garner,
Theresa Tibbets,
Ray and Corrine Burrows

Series Designer
Helen Taylor

Book layout
Macmillan Publishing Solutions

Mixed Sources
Product group from well-managed
forests and other controlled sources
www.fsc.org Cert no. TT-COC-002769
© 1996 Forest Stewardship Council
FSC

Text © 2001, 2009, Chris Webster
Text © 2009, Pam Dowson
© 2009 Scholastic Ltd

Designed using Adobe InDesign

Published by Scholastic Ltd
Villiers House
Clarendon Avenue
Leamington Spa
Warwickshire CV32 5PR

www.scholastic.co.uk

Printed by Bell and Bain Ltd, Glasgow

1 2 3 4 5 6 7 8 9   9 0 1 2 3 4 5 6 7 8

British Library Cataloguing-in-Publication Data
A catalogue record for this book is available from the British Library.

ISBN 978-1407-10118-7

The rights of Chris Webster and Pam Dowson to be identified as the authors
of this work have been asserted by them in accordance with the Copyright,
Designs and Patents Act 1988.

Extracts from the Primary National Strategy's *Primary Framework for
Literacy* (2006) http://nationalstrategies.standards.dcsf.gov.uk/primary/
primaryframework/ © Crown copyright. Reproduced under the terms of the Click
Use Licence.

Acknowledgements
The publishers gratefully acknowledge permission to reproduce the following
copyright material:

David Higham Associates for the use of 'Dreadful Language' by Herbert
Farjeon © Herbert Farjeon. **Egmont UK Ltd** for the use of back cover blurb
from *Mr Gum and the Goblins* by Andy Stanton © 2007 (2007, Egmont UK Ltd).
Macmillan Children's Books for the use of back cover blurb from *The Secret
of the Platform* by Eva Ibbotson © 2001, Eva Ibbotson (2001, Macmillan).
Orion Publishing Group Ltd for the use of back cover blurb from *The Indian in
the Cupboard* by Lynne Reid Banks © 1999, Lynne Reid Banks (2001, Collins).
Penguin Group UK for the use of back cover blurbs from *Driftwood* by Cathy
Cassidy © 2005, Cathy Cassidy (2005, Puffin) and from *The Little Girl and
the Tiny Doll* by Edward and Angela Ardizzone © 1996, Edward and Angela
Ardizzone (2009, Puffin) and for the use of an extract from *A Thief in the
Village and other Stories* by James Berry © 1987, James Berry (1987, Hamish
Hamilton). **Scholastic** for the use of back cover blurb from *Sideways Stories
from Wayside* by Louis Sachar © 2001, Louis Sachar (2001, Scholastic).

Every effort has been made to trace copyright holders for the works reproduced
in this book, and the publishers apologise for any inadvertent omissions.

CONTENTS

INTRODUCTION
100 Literacy Homework Activities: Year 4

About the series

The *100 Literacy Homework Activities* series provides easy-to-use, photocopiable homework sheets for Key Stage 1 and 2 children. Each book in the series contains 100 homework activities that can be embedded into any school homework programme. Each activity sheet provides instructions for the child and a brief note to the helper, stating simply and clearly its purpose and suggesting support and/or further challenge to offer the child. The activities are clearly linked to the renewed Primary Framework for Literacy and are organised by Block (Narrative, Non-fiction, Poetry), then by Unit.

Core skills activities

At the end of each Unit, you will find a number of 'Core skills' activities, designed to support the development of key literacy skills such as word recognition (Years 1 and 2 only), word structure and spelling, and sentence structure and punctuation. Some of the Core skills activities are linked to the content of the units; others are intended to be used for discrete teaching and can be used at any time.

Teachers' notes

The teachers' notes starting on page 8 provide further information about each activity, with notes on setting the homework, differentiation and follow-up work. The Narrative, Non-fiction and Poetry objectives on the teachers' notes show how activities are linked to the Unit plans, while the reference grid on pages 6 and 7 shows how the objectives from Strands 1 to 12 of the Framework are covered in the book. Links to the Scottish curriculum are provided on the Scholastic website (see page 7).

Using the resources

The best way to use these homework resources is to use them flexibly, integrating them with a series of literacy sessions over a number of days. At primary level, homework should be about 'consolidating and reinforcing skills and understanding, particularly in literacy and numeracy' (Department for Children, Schools and Families: Homework Guidelines). Although the homework sheets can be used to support assessment, their main purpose is to reinforce and extend literacy work carried out in class or to help children prepare for upcoming work.

Supporting your helpers

It is vital that parents or carers understand what you are trying to achieve with homework. As well as the 'Dear helper' notes on each sheet, there is a homework diary on page 5 which can be photocopied and sent home with the homework. Multiple copies of these can be fastened together to make a longer term homework record. Discuss with parents/carers what is meant by 'help'. Legitimate help will include sharing the reading of texts, helping to clarify problems, discussing possible answers and so on, but at some stage the child should be left to do his or her best. Tell parents/carers how much time you expect the child to spend on homework. If, after that time, a child is stuck, or has not finished, they should not be forced to continue. Ask parents/carers to write a brief explanation and say that you will give extra help the next day. If children are succeeding with a task and need more time, this can be allowed – but bear in mind that children need a varied and balanced home life!

Using the activities with *100 Literacy Framework Lessons*

Links have been provided on the teachers' notes for those who wish to use the homework activities with the corresponding *100 Literacy Framework Lessons* book. The teachers' notes show if and where a homework task might fit within the context of the appropriate *100 Literacy Framework Lessons* Unit.

 **SCHOLASTIC**
www.scholastic.co.uk

Homework diary

Name of activity	Date sent home	Child's comments		Helper's comments	Teacher's comments
		Did you like this? Tick a face.	**Write one thing you learned**		
		😊 a lot 😐 a little 😞 not much			
		😊 a lot 😐 a little 😞 not much			
		😊 a lot 😐 a little 😞 not much			
		😊 a lot 😐 a little 😞 not much			

Framework objectives

Objectives	Supporting activities (page numbers)
Strand 1: Speaking	
Offer reasons and evidence for their views, considering alternative opinions.	28, 29, 30, 31, 33, 37, 38, 42, 49, 51, 58, 59, 60, 62, 65, 76, 77, 80, 92, 94, 97, 98, 104, 109, 110, 117
Respond appropriately to the contributions of others in the light of differing viewpoints.	51, 58, 59, 61, 94
Tell stories effectively and convey detailed information coherently for listeners.	52, 64, 82, 99, 100
Use and reflect on some ground rules for sustaining talk and interactions.	94
Strand 2: Listening and responding	
Listen to a speaker, make notes on the talk and use notes to develop a role play.	
Compare the different contributions of music, words and images in short extracts from TV programmes.	107, 108
Identify how talk varies with age, familiarity, gender and purpose.	
Strand 3: Group discussion and interaction	
Take different roles in groups and use the language appropriate to them, including the roles of leader, reporter, scribe and mentor.	
Use time, resources and group members efficiently by distributing tasks, checking progress, making back-up plans.	
Identify the main points of each speaker, compare their arguments and how they are presented.	
Strand 4: Drama	
Create roles showing how behaviour can be interpreted from different viewpoints.	53, 62, 63, 71
Develop scripts based on improvisation.	70
Comment constructively on plays and performances, discussing effects and how they are achieved.	73, 107
Strand 6: Word structure and spelling	
Use knowledge of phonics, morphology and etymology to spell new and unfamiliar words.	36, 66, 84, 86, 88, 103, 112, 113, 114, 121, 126, 127
Distinguish the spelling and meaning of common homophones.	66, 86, 87
Know and apply common spelling rules.	36, 66, 86
Develop a range of personal strategies for learning new and irregular words.	36, 88, 103, 113, 114, 126
Strand 7: Understanding and interpreting texts	
Identify and summarise evidence from a text to support a hypothesis.	28, 29, 51, 58, 59, 61, 77, 78, 79, 97, 99, 105, 106
Deduce characters' reasons for behaviour from their actions and explain how ideas are developed in non-fiction texts.	28, 37, 51, 58, 59, 61

📖 SCHOLASTIC
www.scholastic.co.uk

Framework objectives

Objectives	Supporting activities (page numbers)
Strand 7: Understanding and interpreting texts (Cont.)	
Use knowledge of different organisational features of texts to find information effectively.	80, 89, 99
Use knowledge of word structures and origins to develop their understanding of word meanings.	34, 35, 36, 44, 68, 75, 84, 87, 103, 112, 113, 114, 121, 126, 127
Explain how writers use figurative and expressive language to create images and atmosphere.	38, 44, 47, 69, 98, 104, 116, 117, 119, 122, 123, 125
Strand 8: Engaging and responding to texts	
Read extensively favourite authors or genres and experiment with other types of text.	33
Interrogate texts to deepen and clarify understanding and response.	28, 29, 47, 50, 51, 52, 53, 58, 59, 73, 77, 78, 79, 80, 81, 91, 99, 104, 105, 106,111, 119, 122, 123
Explore why and how writers write, including through face-to-face and online contact with authors.	
Strand 9: Creating and shaping texts	
Develop and refine ideas in writing using planning and problem-solving strategies.	31, 32, 39, 40, 41, 43, 63, 65, 72, 93, 100, 110, 124
Use settings and characterisation to engage readers' interest.	32, 39, 40, 51, 64, 65, 71, 72
Summarise and shape material and ideas from different sources to write convincing and informative non-narrative texts.	61, 82, 83, 90, 91, 93, 98, 99, 100, 101, 124
Show imagination through the language used to create emphasis, humour, atmosphere or suspense.	30, 54, 60, 65, 67, 70, 71, 72, 75, 85, 117, 118, 124, 125
Choose and combine words, images and other features for particular effects.	40, 67, 83, 90, 105, 108, 109, 118, 122, 123, 124, 125
Strand 10: Text structure and organisation	
Organise texts into paragraphs to distinguish between different information, events or processes.	41, 42, 43, 76, 90, 92, 101, 106, 110
Use adverbs and conjunctions to establish cohesion within paragraphs.	42, 45, 83, 90, 96, 101, 115
Strand 11: Sentence structure and punctuation	
Clarify meaning and point of view by using varied sentence structure (phrases, clauses and adverbials).	43, 45, 46, 47, 48, 63, 69, 74, 76, 83, 90, 92, 94, 95, 96, 102, 105, 110, 115
Use commas to mark clauses and use the apostrophe for possession.	47, 55, 56, 57, 105, 120
Strand 12: Presentation	
Write consistently with neat, legible and joined handwriting.	
Use wordprocessing packages to present written work and continue to increase speed and accuracy in typing.	

Links to the Scottish curriculum can be found at www.scholastic.co.uk/literacyhomework/y4 (click on Free resources)

Narrative – Unit 1 Stories with historical settings

Page 28 Character quotes
Narrative objective: To write a character sketch using evidence from the text.
Setting the homework: This activity asks children to write about a character from a story that they are reading. Children will need to have plenty of evidence about the character so ensure that enough of the story has been read before setting the task.
Differentiation: All children can attempt this homework. Less confident learners can be helped by being given page numbers to refer to for each section.
Back at school: Share descriptions of different aspects of the character or characters, and the evidence chosen to support it. The next step is to write out the information in essay form.
Link to *100 Literacy Framework Lessons Y4*: NU1, Phase 1: work on characters.

Page 29 Into the shelter again!
Narrative objective: To discuss how differences in time and place are represented.
Setting the homework: Talk to the class about how stories sometimes use specific vocabulary that can give us clues about when and where they are set – they are showing us, not explicitly telling us. This makes it more interesting for the reader – we are like detectives piecing together the story.
Differentiation: An extra note can be sent to helpers of less confident readers, asking them to read the text aloud for the child to spot the clues.
Back at school: Children can compare their solutions with a partner, before whole-class discussion.
Link to *100 Literacy Framework Lessons Y4*: NU1, Phase 1, Day 1: history detectives.

Page 30 Powerful verbs
Narrative objective: To explore the use of powerful verbs.
Setting the homework: Ask the class to give you examples of verbs that can be used in place of *said* or *walked*, noticing how they give more information. Tell them there are more words than they need in the box on the sheet, so they have some choice, or they can use their own ideas.
Differentiation: Less confident readers could be asked to do as many as they can rather than attempt the whole sheet.
Back at school: Pairs of children can compare their choices before a general class feedback and summary, discussing choices.
Link to *100 Literacy Framework Lessons Y4*: NU1, Phases 1 and 2: stories from the 1940s and work on powerful verbs.

Page 31 A character from the past
Narrative objective: To create and develop a main character for a story with a historical setting.
Setting the homework: The children will need to have worked on planning a historical setting for their character to fit into. Remind them of the key aspects of the chosen period and setting and tell them how important it is that their character fits into the setting.
Back at school: Working in small groups, invite the children to describe their characters, using their plan to support their description. Other group members should be encouraged to ask further questions about each others' characters. The characters should then be incorporated into the children's stories.

Page 32 Out of time
Narrative objective: To use a historical setting as a starting point for creating a new story.
Setting the homework: Ask the children to explore the effect of settings on characters by:
- choosing one or more appropriate settings for each character;
- choosing one or more unlikely settings for each character;
- then thinking about how the character would react in each setting and making notes for a story or scene from a story.

Differentiation: Less confident learners could make notes about one match only.
Back at school: Discuss the homework. Ask: *Which combinations of character and setting are silly? Which could be developed into good stories?* (For example: Children – Desert island. This combination was used very effectively in *Lord of the Flies* by William Golding.)

Page 33 What do you like to read? – Core skills

Objective: To experiment with reading a variety of authors and texts.
Setting the homework: Talk with the children about how they choose new books to read. Draw particular attention to the information included in the blurb. Demonstrate how this can be used to help us to decide if we would like a particular book.
Differentiation: Ask helpers of less confident readers to read the blurbs for the child.
Back at school: Ask the children to vote on which books they would choose and encourage volunteers to provide the reasons for their choice.

Page 34 A wet blanket – Core skills

Objective: To explain how writers use figurative language to create images.
Setting the homework: Explain to the children that our language includes many common expressions (sometimes called idioms) which can be quite mystifying until you know them. Encourage the children to guess the meaning of any expression that they do not know before asking their helper.
Differentiation: Most children, and especially EAL learners. will need some help from an adult.
Back at school: Share the definitions of the common expressions and write on the board all the other common expressions that the children found. Children could explore this further by writing a story in which the characters use several common expressions in their speech.

Page 35 Archaic words – Core skills

Objective: To use knowledge of word structures and origins to develop their understanding of word meanings.
Setting the homework: Explain that vocabulary changes over time because:
• many jobs and objects have disappeared
• new jobs and objects have been created
• old words are replaced by new words for the same thing
• fashionable, slang, or dialect words change frequently.
Explain that the children will investigate these changes by highlighting the different kinds of words in different colours so they will need three different coloured pens or pencils.
Back at school: Collect information from the investigation. Add any words that children found out from their parents.

Page 36 Prefix it! – Core skills

Objective: To use knowledge of word structures and origins to develop their understanding of word meanings.
Setting the homework: Revise the term 'prefix' (letters added to the beginning of a word to change its meaning) and 'root' (the basic part of a word), and explain how to play the game.
Differentiation: Write to parents of less confident learners, emphasising how important it is that they understand the meanings of these words.
Back at school: Ensure that the children know the meanings of the words they have made.

Narrative – Unit 2 Stories set in imaginary worlds

Page 37 Alice

Narrative objective: To discuss how settings influence the reactions of characters.
Setting the homework: Talk with the class about the story *Alice in Wonderland* so they understand it is set in an imaginary world. Discuss how Alice's actions are determined by the settings and situations in which she finds herself, and how things happen to her because of the decisions she makes.
Differentiation: Helpers of less confident readers can read the text aloud for them.
Back at school: Ask pairs of children to compare their work before a general whole-class discussion. Children could draw a picture of Alice in the setting as described.

Page 38 Creating an atmosphere

Narrative objective: To express opinions about the mood and atmospheres created by different authors of narratives with fantasy settings.

Setting the homework: Choose a passage to read to the class, inviting their observations about how the writer has created an atmosphere for a particular setting. Tell the children to look for places in the homework text where the writer has deliberately chosen words, phrases or punctuation to help create an atmosphere.

Differentiation: Tell the helpers of less confident readers that they can read the text for the child to spot the features.

Back at school: Pairs of children can compare their findings before feeding back into a whole-class discussion.

Link to *100 Literacy Framework Lessons Y4*: NU2, Phase 1: work on settings and atmosphere.

Page 39 Alien planet

Narrative objective: To create fantasy settings.

Setting the homework: This activity could be used in preparation for Phase 2 of the Unit – creating fantasy settings using photo-editing software. Go over the task, explaining that the pictures are just starting points. If time allows, one of the cards can be used as an example and children can fill out the details in a whole-class discussion.

Differentiation: Less confident learners could develop the card that was the subject of the whole-class discussion, while others should be asked to choose a different setting.

Back at school: Share ideas for developing the settings and ask the children to develop their notes into a detailed description of a setting. When the children come to use their setting in a story, the trick is to pick out parts of the description to use at appropriate times. It is not effective to have all the description in one block.

Link to *100 Literacy Framework Lessons Y4*: NU2, Phase 2: creating settings and atmospheres.

Page 40 Imaginary worlds

Narrative objective: To create fantasy settings.

Setting the homework: Explain to the children that the homework page is a 'toolkit' to help with the drawing of a map. They will also need a piece of blank A3 paper. Drawing the map is the first step in the creation of an imaginary world. Children should note that the pictures for the map include a mix of motives and problems – for example, the elixir of life is a drink that will make people live for ever, but the murky mire is a problem. Encourage the children to use their imagination and add their own ideas. The map can be used for planning stories.

Differentiation: None needed at this stage, though less confident learners will need help when they have to turn their maps into stories and when the stories have to be written down.

Back at school: Share maps and ideas for stories based on them. The next step should be a period of oral preparation in which children make up characters and stories to go with the map and take it in turns to tell them. The final stage is to write the stories.

Page 41 Dinosaur Plateau

Narrative objective: To construct a narrative drawing on common features and themes of stories in fantasy settings.

Setting the homework: Explain that this map provides support for planning a well-structured story. The beginning and end are well defined, and the middle sections can be developed from the many hazards.

Back at school: Children can share and comment on each others' plans. Ask them to refine their plans and begin writing.

Page 42 Dragon slayer

Narrative objective: To organise a story into paragraphs and identify how cohesion is created within and across paragraphs.

Setting the homework: Remind the class about the range of connectives they know. Tell them they will still have many sentences in the piece – they are not trying to join every sentence together! Remind them about how we decide when to start new paragraphs.

Differentiation: Less confident readers could be given a list of possible connectives.

Back at school: Small groups of children can compare their results. Display the text and annotate it with the best or most popular modifications. Children could continue the story.

Page 43 Monty Mouse
Narrative objective: To write narratives arranged into paragraphs.
Setting the homework: Explain that a paragraph is a group of sentences on one topic, or in a story, about one scene. If your school has particular rules for paragraphing, such as leaving a line between paragraphs or using indents, remind the children to use these.
Differentiation: More confident learners could adapt the writing frame by adding paragraphs and using different ways of starting them.
Back at school: Children can apply the paragraphing skills to another story or develop the story.

Page 44 Pirate talk – Core skills
Objective: To show imagination through language used to create emphasis, humour, atmosphere or suspense.
Setting the homework: Revise the term 'synonym'. Explain that a well-chosen synonym of *said* can tell us a great deal about the feelings of the characters speaking.
Differentiation: This sheet is appropriate for children who know and can use some synonyms of *said* such as *asked, cried, declared, exclaimed, replied* and *shouted*. Those who have not mastered these synonyms should be given more work on them instead.
Back at school: Compare the experiments with substituting synonyms in the passage. Sum up by saying that well-written dialogue will include synonyms in the reporting clause (the *said* part of the dialogue) when appropriate, but that they should not be used all the time. Encourage the children to apply the skill of writing dialogue in stories.

Page 45 Quickly – Core skills
Objective: To use adverbs to establish cohesion within paragraphs.
Setting the homework: Revise the meaning of the term *adverb* using the explanation shown.
Differentiation: A full understanding of all the different kinds of adverbs (time, place, manner, degree) is difficult, but common '-ly' adverbs are easy to use and identify because of the ending.
Back at school: Discuss the different adverbs that children used and check that they found all the adverbs in the example paragraph. If the children are working on a piece of narrative writing, encourage them to redraft their writing by seeing if an adverb would improve the description. Point out that although the '-ly' suffix is a useful way of identifying an adverb, not all adverbs have '-ly' endings. For example, *well, often* and *sideways* are all adverbs.

Page 46 Adverb attack – Core skills
Objective: To use adverbs to establish cohesion within paragraphs.
Setting the homework: Revise the term 'adverb' and use the example to show where the adverb is usually placed.
Back at school: Apply this skill to the context of writing a story with dialogue as soon as possible after the homework.

Page 47 Punctuation posers – Core skills
Objective: To clarify meaning and point of view by using varied sentence structure.
Setting the homework: Remind the children that a complex sentence includes a main clause (that makes sense on its own) and a subordinate clause (that gives more information about the main clause).
Differentiation: Children who are not yet secure about complex sentences should be given more basic work identifying the components of complex sentences.
Back at school: Ask selected children to write one sentence each as they have done in their homework, while the others check their own work. Discuss any problems that arise. Encourage and monitor the children's use of complex sentences in their writing.

Page 48 All in a good clause – Core skills
Objective: To clarify meaning and point of view by using varied sentence structure.
Setting the homework: Revise the necessary key terms – for example, *sentence, complex sentence, main clause, subordinate clause, subject, verb*. Go over the explanation. Though the terminology is difficult, the task is quite easy. So, even if the terminology doesn't come easily, the children will develop an implicit knowledge of the concept.
Differentiation: Even at this level, clause analysis is difficult and abstract. It is not suitable for children who have not grasped basics. Less confident learners could be given simpler, related work, such as joining clauses with connectives in a simple pre-set pattern.
Back at school: Go over the exercise and consolidate with similar work.

Narrative – Unit 3 Stories from other cultures

Page 49 Fanso and Granny-Flo
Narrative objective: To identify expressive and descriptive language used to describe an unfamiliar setting.
Setting the homework: Tell the children that they will be looking for clues that help them to create a picture of the setting in which the story is told. Some are more obvious than others – they should think about what the characters are doing as well as straightforward descriptions.
Differentiation: Helpers of less confident learners can read the passage aloud before discussing the clues with the child.
Back at school: Pairs of children can compare their results before a general class discussion. Were there any words or phrases that the children did not know?
Link to *100 Literacy Framework Lessons Y4*: NU3, Phase 1, Day 1: looking for clues to show a story is not from the UK.

Page 50 Story research
Narrative objective: To research background information – for example, about the country where the story is set.
Setting the homework: This activity should be linked to a class story. You will need to have already read all or part of a story with the children and identified the country in which it is set. You may wish to provide photocopied resources such as maps to aid their search.
Differentiation: More confident readers may like to provide extra information.
Back at school: Children can share information in small groups, with one spokesperson from each group feeding back to the whole class. Collated information could be displayed along with a map of the country to support further work.
Link to *100 Literacy Framework Lessons Y4*: NU3, Phase 1, Day 3: researching.

Page 51 Banja's coming of age
Narrative objective: To compare customs and beliefs in a story from another culture with their own.
Setting the homework: After reading the story, ask the children to discuss the questions at the top of the page with their helper. This will help them develop empathy with the Kung people, and in particular, with Banja, a young person 'coming of age' in his society.
Differentiation: More confident learners could be asked to carry out the extension activity. The continuation should be another episode in Banja's trial – not necessarily the whole story.
Back at school: Discuss the questions at the top of the page. Ask children who have undertaken the extension activity to share some of the continuations and discuss how well they fit what we already know of Banja and his environment.

Page 52 Character interview
Narrative objective: To select a character from a story and demonstrate how to devise questions to ask that character.
Setting the homework: The children should know your chosen class story well before doing this activity. Talk with them about who the key characters are, and set them thinking about the kinds of things they might want to know about them, based on the story itself.
Differentiation: You may wish to send home a brief written synopsis, or key word notes, of the story for children who are less confident in speaking and listening.
Back at school: Children can compare their questions and discuss their usefulness.
Link to *100 Literacy Framework Lessons Y4*: NU3, Phase 3, Day 2: making deductions about characters.

Page 53 In the hot-seat

Narrative objective: To be interviewed in role by a partner.

Setting the homework: Ensure all children have their original questions from page 52 'Character interview' to take home with this activity. They may need to redraft some of the questions first in order to prepare for useful and informative answers.

Differentiation: Less confident writers may need help in redrafting their questions.

Back at school: Some children may like to read out their written responses, in role. Pairs of children can re-enact the hot-seating activity, perhaps followed up by performances for the rest of the class to appraise.

Link to *100 Literacy Framework Lessons Y4*: NU3, Phase 3, Day 2: making deductions about characters.

Page 54 Crocodile river – Core skills

Objective: To choose and combine words for particular effects.

Setting the homework: Use the example to explain how some verbs are more powerful than others in specific contexts. Often, the verb that first comes to mind simply describes the action. Ask the children to double-check that the words they have used to fill the gaps are verbs.

Differentiation: All children should attempt this task.

Back at school: Share the different words used and 'weigh' each one to discuss its power and effectiveness.

Page 55 Jason's flying saucer – Core skills

Objective: To use the apostrophe for possession.

Setting the homework: Go over the explanation on the page. Point out that the apostrophe should be placed above a small gap just before the 's'. The possessive apostrophe can be difficult to teach, the main problem being that some children will use an apostrophe with every word ending in 's'. One way to help is to focus on the use of the possessive apostrophe for people (and creatures). This homework covers the singular use only.

Differentiation: This is a game which all children can enjoy and succeed at. More confident learners could be introduced to the plural possessive apostrophe by including some plural cards, such as *sailors/ships, girls/changing rooms*.

Back at school: Monitor the use of the possessive apostrophe in writing. Be rigorous in correcting misuse of the apostrophe. One of the reasons it is badly used by older children (and adults) is that placing it before any 's' becomes a habit.

Page 56 Phantom phrases – Core skills

Objective: To use commas when adding phrases and clauses to sentences.

Setting the homework: This homework should be used as part of a series of lessons on sentence building. It focuses on the phrase in apposition and how to punctuate it. Explain that a phrase in apposition is extra description added to a sentence between two commas.

Differentiation: This is essentially a cloze exercise with all the possible answers listed above. Ask less confident learners to do half of the passage.

Back at school: Discuss which phrases fit which gaps. Encourage the children to use phrases in apposition to enhance descriptions.

Page 57 Whose is it? – Core skills

Objective: To revise the use of the apostrophe for possession.

Setting the homework: Go through the explanation and the examples and check to see that the children fully understand them.

Differentiation: Less confident learners should concentrate on one or two of the rules.

Back at school: Check the children's work either individually or as a group. Encourage the children to look at their use of the apostrophe in their writing.

Narrative – Unit 4 Stories which raise issues/dilemmas

Page 58 Bina's betrothal

Narrative objective: To predict the outcome of an issue or dilemma.

Setting the homework: This extract raises the issues of arranged marriages. It is worth pointing out to all children, whatever their cultural background, that most societies have practised arranged marriages at some time in their history (it was common in England until the nineteenth century). Also, it is worth challenging the assumption that marrying for love is always preferable to an arranged marriage – witness the high divorce rate in Western European society today when people choose their mates. The issue should be discussed in the context of the story. Bina stands to lose a great deal if she goes against her community. Is it worth it? Explain that the purpose of the discussion is to provide ideas for the next episode in the story.

Differentiation: More confident learners could be asked to carry out the extension activity.

Back at school: Ask children who have undertaken the extension activity to share their next episodes. Discuss the issues raised in these episodes. The story could be further developed so that it has a conclusion that shows the wisdom or otherwise of Bina's choice.

Link to *100 Literacy Framework Lessons Y4*: NU4, Phase 1: identifying issues and dilemmas and exploring possible courses of action.

Page 59 Lost wallet

Narrative objective: To explore possible courses of action and to write own endings.

Setting the homework: Encourage the children to discuss the questions at the top of the page with their helper before doing the written task.

Differentiation: This activity is similar to page 61, 'Death by water', except that the issue it raises is less abstract. It can, therefore, be used at the same time as page 61 for less confident learners, or as a preparation for page 61.

Back at school: Share some of the plans for story endings and discuss further the issues raised.

Link to *100 Literacy Framework Lessons Y4*: NU4, Phase 1: identifying issues and dilemmas and exploring possible course of action.

Page 60 The best words

Narrative objective: To use words that describe atmosphere and emotions in relation to a character facing a dilemma.

Setting the homework: Remind the children about the language used in stories they have been working on in class, where the writer has deliberately chosen words to convey tension when a character faces a dilemma. Encourage them to find a variety of words, avoiding repetition.

Differentiation: Less confident writers could write single words only.

Back at school: In groups, children can share their ideas, reporting their favourite examples back to the whole class. The best can be displayed for use in later writing. Stories could be fully developed and written up.

Page 61 Death by water

Narrative objective: To focus on a problem faced by a main character and to discuss alternative views on the problem.

Setting the homework: The extract is from a story about the famous fortune teller Michele de Notredame (known as Nostradamus) who lived from 1503–66. Nostradamus is said to have predicted many historical events including the World Wars. Encourage the children to discuss the questions at the top of the page with their helper before doing the written task.

Differentiation: More confident learners could discuss the issue of fate in a short essay. Less confident learners could be asked to show their understanding of the issue by planning a continuation to the story which shows whether it is possible to tell the future, or sensible to believe fortune-tellers. Alternatively, they could do page 59, 'Lost wallet', instead in which the issue for discussion is less abstract.

Back at school: Share some of the essays and continuations and discuss the issues raised.

Page 62 What do you think?

Narrative objective: To discuss how characters might react to particular issues or dilemmas.
Setting the homework: Tell the children that there will be more than one possible reaction from the characters to their particular situation, and they should discuss them all. They should think about what the best decisions would be.
Back at school: Children can retell their rehearsed story to a partner. Have a discussion about right and wrong decisions (particularly in relation to the bullying scenario), and potential consequences of the characters' actions. You could use the drama technique 'conscience alley' to focus more closely on each situation.

Page 63 My advice is...

Narrative objective: To write in role as a character from the story, advising the main character about what they should do.
Setting the homework: Discuss with the class some texts they could use (including suitable TV programmes) or suggest a text you are working on together (such as page 61 'Death by water'). Ensure they understand what sort of problems or dilemmas they could focus on, and remind them they will be writing in role as another character in the story.
Differentiation: You could provide sentence starters for less confident writers, or suggest they record their advice.
Back at school: In pairs, children can role play giving and receiving the advice.

Page 64 A good start

Narrative objective: To demonstrate how to write the opening part of the story to set the scene and consider ways to draw the reader in.
Setting the homework: Read some story openings where settings are used, to demonstrate various ways writers grab the reader's attention. Ask the children to identify what makes the openings work. Remind them not to use clichéd openings, such as *One day...*
Differentiation: Less confident writers may like to draw the setting on the back of the sheet before writing.
Back at school: Ask the children to read out their openings to partners or in small groups. Listeners can report good points to the whole class.

Page 65 Alternative endings

Narrative objectives: To write own endings based on discussion. To compare these endings with the original story ending and evaluate it.
Setting the homework: Remind the children of the basic story of 'Goldilocks and the Three Bears'. Talk about how Goldilocks's reaction to the dilemma of being discovered is simply to run away. Tell them they will be writing an alternative ending where the dilemma is solved differently, so they have to consider the consequences.
Differentiation: Less confident writers could make storyboards with simple captions.
Back at school: Children can compare their alternative versions in small groups, commenting on each others' work.

Page 66 I see the sea – Core skills

Objective: To distinguish the spelling and meaning of common homophones.
Setting the homework: Point out that homophones have a valuable purpose: the different spellings help avoid confusion about meaning.
Differentiation: Children who make mistakes after this homework should be given more practice.
Back at school: Monitor mistakes caused by confusion about homophones in children's written work.

Page 67 Fussy werewolf – Core skills

Objective: To show imagination through language used to create emphasis, humour, atmosphere or suspense.
Setting the homework: Revise the term 'adjective' using the explanation and examples on the page.
Back at school: Select some children to read out the passage with their chosen adjectives. Discuss the effectiveness of the adjectives and perhaps decide on a class version that could be displayed.

Page 68 A sitting duck – Core skills
Objective: To use knowledge of word structures and origins to develop their understanding of word meanings.
Setting the homework: Explain that common sayings and clichés are often used by adults, but can be mystifying to children and foreigners learning the language. Tell the children that if they do not know the meaning of a saying, they should ask an adult.
Differentiation: Children who do not start off with a knowledge of at least some of the sayings could be asked to find out about any five of them. If appropriate dictionaries are not available, the children should be encouraged to ask others for the meanings.
Back at school: Discuss what the sayings mean and talk about contexts in which they may be used.

Page 69 Add an adverb – Core skills
Objective: To use adverbs to establish cohesion within paragraphs.
Setting the homework: Revise the terms 'verb' and 'adverb'. Explain that a well-chosen adverb can enhance the descriptive power of a piece of writing.
Differentiation: Children who do not understand the terms 'verb' and 'adverb' should be given reinforcement work on those terms and do this homework later.
Back at school: Share adverbs and ask the children to add any new ones they like to their list. This homework is most effective in a lesson or series of lessons that teach children how to improve description. Rather than it being a one-off, repeat this homework with other verbs, so that the children build up a bank of verbs with suitable adverbs.

Narrative – Unit 5 Plays

Page 70 Improvisation
Narrative objective: To improvise dialogue between key characters and use this as the basis for writing own short playscripts, using features explored earlier.
Setting the homework: Ensure all the children have a copy of page 62, 'What do you think?'. Explain what improvisation is, and model it using one of the scenarios on the sheet. Remind the children how to write dialogue as a script, using stage directions.
Differentiation: Less confident readers could be given extra ideas for some of the scenarios, and helped to devise a list of key words to take home.
Back at school: Children can perform their scenes with a partner.
Link to *100 Literacy Framework Lessons Y4*: NU5, Phase 3: improvising and planning playscripts.

Page 71 Goldilocks – the play
Narrative objective: To improvise dialogue between key characters and use this as the basis for writing own short playscripts.
Setting the homework: Ensure the children have their copies of the homework from page 65 'Alternative endings' which they will use as the basis for this playscript. Remind them about the kinds of stage directions they should use, and encourage them to read and edit their work before deciding on their final version.
Back at school: Small groups of children can share and rehearse each others' scenes with some being chosen for performance to the whole class, who can evaluate them if appropriate.
Link to *100 Literacy Framework Lessons Y4*: NU5, Phase 3: improvising and planning playscripts.

Page 72 Pantomime planner
Narrative objective: To create a play version of a known narrative.
Setting the homework: The idea is to stimulate ideas for the playscript of a pantomime which should be modern and different from the traditional pantomime.
Differentiation: Children of all abilities will be able to contribute imaginative ideas.
Back at school: When writing the final draft of the playscript ensure that the appropriate conventions are followed.

www.scholastic.co.uk

Page 73 Toys alive!

Narrative objective: To read, explore, perform and evaluate playscripts.

Setting the homework: The children should already have had some experience of reading playscripts before doing this activity, and should understand the function of stage directions. Tell them to practise all the parts, taking turns with a helper (or helpers), so they are ready to perform it with a group back at school.

Differentiation: Less confident readers could concentrate on reading Drag-along dog's lines, which are slightly easier.

Back at school: Assign parts to groups of children for them to rehearse and perform. The class should evaluate each performance, offering positive and helpful comments. They could also write the rest of the scene.

Page 74 Turn it down! – Core skills

Objective: To clarify meaning and point of view by using varied sentence structure.

Setting the homework: Go over the four different types of sentences. Emphasise that questions must always end with a question mark. The use of exclamation marks often depends on how something is said or written. If a sentence is meant to convey excitement or urgency, it should end with an exclamation mark.

Differentiation: Less confident learners should focus on the use of the question and exclamation mark. More confident learners could analyse the different types of sentence by looking for patterns in the order of subject (S), verb (V) and object (O).

Back at school: Ask the children to find the four types of sentence in books they are reading.

Page 75 Sleeping Beauty – Core skills

Objective: To show imagination through language used to create emphasis, humour, atmosphere or suspense.

Setting the homework: Ensure that the children understand the term 'synonym'. Explain that they should avoid choosing words which are boring (*nice*), inappropriate (*guy*), or repetitive (*prickly* in both the third and fourth sentences).

Differentiation: More confident learners could be encouraged to find their own synonyms to fill the gaps.

Back at school: Discuss the synonyms chosen by the children and their reasons for choosing them.

Non-fiction – Unit 1 Recounts: Newspapers/magazines

Page 76 Meet the deadline!

Non-fiction objectives: To ask and answer: Who? What? Why? Where? When? To write a simple recount.

Setting the homework: You can use this activity alongside page 80, 'Six honest men'. Tell the children that they need to decide in which order to write up the information – it doesn't have to follow the pattern given, but all should be included in their final piece.

Differentiation: Provide some sentence starters for less confident writers.

Back at school: In pairs, each child takes turn as the 'editor', reading their partner's article and giving them feedback. Good examples can be shared with the class.

Page 77 Fact or opinion?

Non-fiction objective: To read and discuss *fact* and *opinion* in a recount.

Setting the homework: Ensure the children know the difference between facts and opinions. They should be able to find, or know how to find evidence for facts. There are key words they can look out for in relation to opinions, such as *thought, might have* or *probably*.

Differentiation: Helpers can read the text aloud for less confident readers.

Back at school: Ask the children to compare their results before general class feedback. Ask where the evidence is found for the facts, and list the key words that pointed to opinions.

Link to *100 Literacy Framework Lessons Y4*: NFU1, Phase 2: discussing fact and opinion.

Page 78 A loaded gun?
Non-fiction objective: To read and discuss *fact* and *opinion* in a newspaper article.
Setting the homework: Define *fact* and *opinion*. Use the first three sentences of the article to explain the difference.
Differentiation: Less confident learners should find the facts first. They should also be able to find some of the more obvious opinions. More confident learners should be able to find the opinions which are less obvious.
Back at school: Highlight fact and opinion during a follow-up discussion. The lesson can then be developed, or the skills transferred to another topic.
Link to *100 Literacy Framework Lessons Y4*: NFU1, Phase 2: discussing fact and opinion.

Page 79 Newspaper features
Non-fiction objective: To analyse newspaper texts, revising key organisational features and identifying language conventions.
Setting the homework: Ask parents to provide two newspapers that are as different as possible. If parents are reluctant to buy newspapers, they can use free local newspapers but they should bear in mind that these often contain more advertising than standard daily papers. Enlarge this homework page to A3 to allow more space for writing.
Differentiation: Less confident learners could be asked to focus on the first two sections only.
Back at school: Discuss the comparisons between different newspapers.
Link to *100 Literacy Framework Lessons Y4*: NFU1, Phase 3, Days 1 and 2: features of newspaper articles.

Page 80 Six honest men
Non-fiction objective: To analyse newspaper or magazine texts, revising key features.
Setting the homework: Tell the children to look for answers to each question one at a time – such as all the 'what?' questions first. Their notes should be brief answers to each question. If there are any they can't find answers for, they should leave them blank.
Differentiation: You may wish to supply a selection of simpler texts for less confident readers to choose from.
Back at school: Ask the children to share their answers. Which questions did they find most answers for? Which gave least information? Which would they use first in an article they write themselves?

Page 81 What's in the news?
Non-fiction objective: To analyse newspaper texts, revising key organisational features and identifying language conventions.
Setting the homework: The children should be familiar with the features they are looking for in the text, so that this is a reinforcement of work already done in class. They could use highlighter pens of different colours for past tense and third person, if appropriate.
Differentiation: You may wish to ask some children to look for just the first three features.
Back at school: Use an enlarged version of the text for children to highlight examples of each feature, against which they can check their own work.
Link to *100 Literacy Framework Lessons Y4*: NFU1, Phase 3, Days 1 and 2: features of newspaper articles.

Page 82 The Giant's Grave
Non-fiction objective: To redraft a recount into a newspaper article.
Setting the homework: The children should have had some experience of analysing the style of newspaper articles, knowing, for example, that the article usually starts with the end of the story; giving the game away right at the beginning.
Differentiation: Helpers of less confident readers can read the text aloud for them. Some writers might find to easier to draw a picture, with appropriate captions.
Back at school: Ask a few children to read out their articles, after practising reading to a partner. Encourage them to evaluate how successful they were in writing a newspaper article rather than a normal story.
Link to *100 Literacy Framework Lessons Y4*: NFU1, Phase 3: rewriting a recount as a newspaper article.

Page 83 Be a newspaper editor

Non-fiction objective: To redraft a newspaper article.
Setting the homework: Go over the task and the suggestions. Explain that, as the editor, it is their decision how to shorten the article. The main decision will be whether to leave out whole sections, or to try to keep everything in, though in a shorter form. Ask the children to count the number of words in their final version.
Differentiation: Less confident learners should cut whole sections rather than try to summarise everything.
Back at school: Discuss the task and different possible solutions to it.

Page 84 Verbalise it! – Core skills

Objective: To use knowledge of word structures to develop their understanding of meanings.
Setting the homework: Explain that nouns and adjectives can be changed into verbs by following certain patterns. Explain that the task is to match the nouns and adjectives to the verbs, then look for patterns in the way the words have been changed.
Differentiation: More confident learners could also be asked to distinguish between the nouns and adjectives in column one.
Back at school: Emphasise the patterns of changes that children have found.

Page 85 Got a nice garden – Core skills

Objective: To show imagination through language used to create emphasis, humour, atmosphere or suspense.
Setting the homework: It is important to tell the children that there is nothing wrong with the words *nice* and *got* – they are perfectly correct English. However, they are overused.
Differentiation: The 'got' sentences are more difficult as some of them need rephrasing. Less confident learners could be asked to do the first three only.
Back at school: Share the different words that children thought of. Do the same activity with other overused words.

Page 86 Boy overboard! – Core skills

Objective: To distinguish the meaning and spelling of common homophones.
Setting the homework: Explain that differences in spelling are used to show differences in meaning in many words that sound the same. This is often used to create jokes.
Differentiation: Some children may be able to describe the different meanings of the homophones to their helper, but not be able to spell them. In this case, the helper could write the word first and the child after.
Back at school: Go over the homophones, then share the humorous sentences that children made up. Monitor children's writing for confusion between words with the same sound but different spelling.

Page 87 Homophone cards – Core skills

Objective: To distinguish the meaning and spelling of common homophones.
Setting the homework: Explain that homophones, though they sometimes cause spelling problems, are helpful as they remind us of different meanings. For example, a television *programme* is spelled differently to a computer *program*. It is also worth pointing out that homophones are used to make up jokes (when they are called puns), such as *Is a vicar's budgie a bird of pray?*
Differentiation: Less confident learners could be given sheets with the more difficult words deleted, such as *principal/principle, profit/prophet*.
Back at school: Create an interactive homophone display using the cards. Encourage the children to add more homophones.

Non-fiction – Unit 2 Information texts

Page 88 Phantom pharaohs
Non-fiction objective: To use third and fourth place letters to locate and sequence words in alphabetical order.
Setting the homework: Explain the principle of using second, third and fourth place letters to arrange words alphabetically. Tell the children that they should think of their own definitions first. If they do not know a word, they can look it up in a dictionary, but they must write the definition using their words.
Differentiation: Children who are still vague about the alphabet should be given basic work alphabetising by first letters.
Back at school: Display the sorted list so children can check their alphabetical order. Discuss the definitions. A follow-up would be to write an alliterative poem or story using some of the words.
Link to *100 Literacy Framework Lessons Y4*: NFU2, Phase 1: dictionary and thesaurus work.

Page 89 The resort of the millennium
Non-fiction objective: To locate key words or phrases, headings, lists, bullet points, captions and key sentences to appraise their usefulness in supporting the reader to gain information effectively.
Setting the homework: The homework is a non-fiction text in the form of a magazine article about Porto Paso. It can be used as an example of 'signposting' in non-fiction. Explain the task. A helpful way to answer the second question is to compare this kind of text with a text that is just words (no headings and so on).
Back at school: Display the different examples of non-fiction texts brought in and discuss their signposting.

Page 90 Porto Paso report
Non-fiction objective: To develop and refine ideas in writing.
Setting the homework: Explain that the report refers to the Porto Paso development plan on page 89, 'The resort of the millennium'. Page 89 should be given to the children along with this one. Children should imagine how the development has progressed. As long as what they write fits the basic facts on page 89, they have a completely free rein: their report can be positive or negative.
Differentiation: Less confident learners could be given a modified page with fewer sections.
Back at school: Share the reports and discuss the differences.

Page 91 Non-fiction review
Non-fiction objective: To appraise books for their usefulness in supporting the reader to gain information effectively.
Setting the homework: Ask the children to fill in the second section during the lesson to help them remember which books they used. Give the children A3 copies of the page or ask them to use both sides.
Differentiation: Less confident learners should review two books only.
Back at school: Discuss the qualities of a good non-fiction book and the process of retrieving information.
Link to *100 Literacy Framework Lessons Y4*: NFU2, Phase 2: appraising non-fiction texts.

Page 92 Flying machines
Non-fiction objective: To identify how paragraphs are used to organise and sequence information.
Setting the homework: Go over the explanation. In particular, ensure that children understand the difference between indented and blocked paragraphs. The task provides practice in layout of paragraphs, grouping information by topic, and adding subheadings.
Differentiation: Emphasise to less confident learners that there are four paragraphs – an introduction and a description of three different kinds of flying machine: balloon, aeroplane, rocket. More confident learners could add additional paragraphs of information about jet aircraft, jumbo jets, supersonic aircraft, and so on.
Back at school: Briefly discuss how children paragraphed the text and the subheadings they chose. Then, apply the skill to writing a real piece of research in paragraphs.

Page 93 Legend or history?

Non-fiction objective: To fill out brief notes into connected prose.

Setting the homework: Introduce or revise the term 'prose'. Prose is ordinary writing in sentences – contrast with poetry. Then hold a class discussion to elicit general background information about Robin Hood. Introduce the question: *Is the story of Robin Hood a legend or is it based on history?* Explain that the task is to put the notes into sentences. The following can be given as an example: *Robin Hood was an earl who was made an outlaw and went to live in Sherwood Forest.* Explain that children who have extra information, or who are keen to find out, may include it, but that it is not essential. The task will be judged on how well the notes are made into connected prose.

Differentiation: Less confident learners should write down the example given above, and use it both as a starting point and a model. More confident learners should add to the notes from their own knowledge and research before turning them into connected prose.

Back at school: Invite some children to read out their short articles and ask the class to evaluate each one, on the smoothness of the prose.

Link to *100 Literacy Framework Lessons Y4*: NFU2, Phase 2: writing connected prose from notes.

Page 94 Only connect – Core skills

Objective: To use connectives (conjunctions) to establish cohesion.

Setting the homework: This homework is mainly oral. Give the children a topic to discuss, such as school uniform, fox hunting or recycling. They should read through the list of connectives and discuss the topic with their helper, jotting down any other connectives that arise in the discussion. Finally, they can make notes in preparation for writing on the topic.

Back at school: Make a list of all the additional connectives. Re-run the discussion, continuing to add to the list as new connectives arise. Finally, ask the children to copy all the connectives they do not have, thus making a valuable resource to support their own writing.

Page 95 Join it – Core skills

Objective: To use connectives (conjunctions) to establish cohesion.

Setting the homework: Revise the term 'connective': connectives are joining words. There are two types of connective: coordinating, which join clauses with equal weight and subordinating, which join a clause of lesser importance to the main clause. Ask children to look at the list of connectives on the sheet. Ask: *Can they remember which connectives are coordinating connectives and which are subordinating connectives?*

Back at school: Discuss which connectives work best in each sentence.

Page 96 Using connectives – Core skills

Objective: To use connectives (conjunctions) to establish cohesion.

Setting the homework: Ensure that the children understand the word *connective*. You might wish to model the activity.

Back at school: Share some examples of statements joined by connectives and children's own sentences. If time allows, take the idea a step further by experimenting with joining three statements.

Non-fiction – Unit 3 Explanation texts

Page 97 Which is which?

Non-fiction objective: To distinguish between explanatory texts, reports and recounts.

Setting the homework: You should have done some preparatory work on the three text types, to ensure children have some familiarity with the criteria in the boxes on the sheet. It would be a good idea to go over the grid to clarify any statements children may be unclear about.

Back at school: Groups of children can compare their responses, providing explanations for their choices, particularly where they differ from their partner's. Ask for feedback to the whole class, discussing different reasons for the choices made, and agreeing answers.

Link to *100 Literacy Framework Lessons Y4*: NFU3, Phase 1: examining features of recounts, reports and explanations.

Page 98 A load of rubbish!

Non-fiction objective: To develop awareness of the language features of an explanation text.

Setting the homework: Explain that the sentences on the sheet are in the wrong order for the explanation to make sense, so the children should cut them out and try different ways of re-ordering them so that the process is explained clearly. Ask what kinds of words might give them clues. A second sheet of paper is needed.

Differentiation: Helpers may need to read the sentences for some children.

Back at school: Pairs of children should compare their results before a general class discussion. Children should explain what word clues they used in making their decisions. Agree the best order.

Link to *100 Literacy Framework Lessons Y4*: NFU3, Phases 2 and 3: explaining a process.

Page 99 Researching rubbish

Non-fiction objective: To use a plan and oral rehearsal to support the writing of an explanation text.

Setting the homework: Ensure the children know they are only making brief notes, which will be used to support an oral explanation. The class can share ideas for places where they can find the information they need. You could acquire council leaflets on recycling to send home with the activity.

Back at school: Children use their notes to give an oral explanation to a partner, who can be encouraged to evaluate against criteria for the text type. Some children can repeat their explanations for the whole class.

Link to *100 Literacy Framework Lessons Y4*: NFU3, Phase 3: producing oral explanations.

Page 100 Crystal clear

Non-fiction objective: To write explanatory texts from a plan, using the conventions modelled in shared writing.

Setting the homework: Ensure all children have their notes from page 99, 'Researching rubbish'. They could repeat their oral explanations as revision and reinforcement. Go over with the class the criteria for an explanation text.

Differentiation: Less confident writers could make a simple bullet-pointed list.

Back at school: Ask pairs of children to work together on each other's writing, using an editing process to redraft the letters on a separate sheet of paper. Afterwards, have a class discussion on what was easy and what was difficult about writing explanation texts.

Link to *100 Literacy Framework Lessons Y4*: NFU3, Phase 2: writing explanatory texts in the form of a letter.

Page 101 Flushed with success

Non-fiction objective: Use paragraphs, connectives and the other key language and structural features appropriate to explanatory writing.

Setting the homework: Explain that the text is a first draft of an explanation. The ideas have been written down quickly, but need redrafting to make them clear. Go over the task which explains clearly what must be done to turn this first draft into a clear explanation. Connect the first few statements to give an example of how to fill the gaps.

Differentiation: This is a difficult exercise as the text has to be provided with link words and phrases, paragraphs and subheadings. Less confident learners could be given a version of the sheet that includes the link words and phrases so that they just need to complete the paragraphing task.

Back at school: Go over the passage and then apply the skill to redrafting the non-fiction work in progress.

Page 102 Oddly shaped – Core skills

Objective: To choose and combine words, images and other features for particular effects.

Setting the homework: Go over the explanation on the page. For more confident children, explain the terms 'phrase' and 'clause' and that adjectives can appear as single words, phrases, or clauses. Explain that some of the phrases on the page will fit more than one of the sentences, so they should try to find a suitable adjectival phrase for each sentence without using any of the phrases twice.

Differentiation: Though the concept of adjectival phrases is difficult, the task on the page is fairly easy, so almost all children will benefit from attempting it.

Back at school: Briefly go over the adjectival phrases. Discuss what happens if the sentences and the phrases are swapped round. Encourage the children to use adjectival phrases in their creative writing.

Page 103 Word clusters – Core skills
Objective: To use knowledge of phonics, morphology and etymology to spell new and unfamiliar words.
Setting the homework: Talk about the example *electric* and explain how the addition of different prefixes and suffixes have been used to make related words.
Differentiation: Less confident learners could be asked to do just one of the words. More confident learners could be asked to tackle the extension activity.
Back at school: Share the word clusters. Who found the most words for each cluster? What other words and word clusters did they find?

Non-fiction – Unit 4 Persuasive texts

Page 104 Skyliner
Non-fiction objective: To express views about the persuasive nature of different texts.
Setting the homework: This page can be used by itself or as part of a series of exercises (pages 104, 105 and 106) about the imaginary Skyliner. Together, these pages set up an imaginary situation that can be used as a stimulus for a range of writing. Ask the children to read the advertisement carefully. When highlighting things that are persuasive, they should think about the features that they would find most attractive, such as the glass-bottomed swimming pool. To do the second task, they need to look very carefully at the advertisement as a whole (but don't mention the small print at this stage).
Back at school: Discuss the advertisement. Use the tasks at the top of the page as a focus for discussion. Broaden the discussion to include real advertisements. Follow up the study of real advertisements by asking children to design their own.

Page 105 Skyliner complaint
Non-fiction objective: To express views about the persuasive nature of different texts.
Setting the homework: Review the Skyliner advertisement on page 104. Tell the children that the homework involves evaluating a letter of complaint from a customer who has just returned from a holiday on Skyliner. Explain that they will need both the advertisement and the letter to carry out the activity. Remind them to look carefully at the small print in the advertisement.
Differentiation: Less confident learners could focus on the first and third tasks only.
Back at school: Discuss whether the complaints are fair. Share some of the replies. (Many of the complaints are justified because of the small print that restricted some of the service to first class only. However, it is probably unfair to complain about a crowded observation deck as everybody would want to see New York. Also, it is reasonable to expect to pay more for food prepared and served in the sky.) Follow up by asking children to write letters of complaint in another context.

Page 106 Unsafe at any speed
Non-fiction objective: To identify elements of a text that would persuade a reader.
Setting the homework: This page can be used by itself or with page 110 'Five-point plan'. Go over the tasks at the top of the page. If using this page with page 110, ask children to note how each paragraph fits the five-point plan.
Differentiation: Less confident learners could focus on the first and second tasks only.
Back at school: Discuss what children have learned from studying this argumentative article and apply this knowledge to the writing of an argumentative article on another topic.

Page 107 Film trailers
Non-fiction objective: To identify elements of a film trailer that would persuade a reader to see a film.
Setting the homework: Some introductory work should have been done on the effects of music in film, and on understanding what a voice-over is. Children with internet access could use the site at www.filmstreet.co.uk where up-to-date film trailers for children can be found. You should tell the children that they should choose films designed for children.
Back at school: Children can use their completed sheets to tell a partner about the persuasive elements in the film trailer they watched, before a general class discussion.
Link to *100 Literacy Framework Lessons Y4*: NFU4, Phase 1, Days 4 to 7: analysing trailers.

Page 108 Voice-over

Non-fiction objective: To write a voice-over script to persuade a reader to see a film; to combine words, music and images to convince the reader.

Setting the homework: Show the class a film trailer, noting the length of each scene and the amount of voice-over that goes with them. They should have already done some preparatory work on how music and sound effects work in film trailers.

Differentiation: Some children may find it easier to record their work in the form of a storyboard.

Back at school: Pairs of children can compare their sheets before performing their voice-overs for each other to comment on.

Link to *100 Literacy Framework Lessons Y4*: NFU4, Phase 2: creating trailers.

Page 109 Film poster

Non-fiction objective: To choose and combine words and images for particular effects.

Setting the homework: Talk with the class about some of the films they might choose, concentrating on films for children. Tell them to avoid choosing films they do not know very well. Talk about the layout of posters generally, as well as specific information and language that might be used in advertising a film.

Differentiation: Some children may benefit from having a list of suitable words to choose from.

Back at school: Keep a space where the completed posters can be displayed. Children can comment on their effectiveness.

Page 110 Five-point plan

Non-fiction objective: To plan the presentation of a point of view.

Setting the homework: Enlarge the page to A3 to provide more room for writing, or ask children to write on separate sheets of paper. All the preparatory research and discussion about the topic will need to have been done so that children have a point of view to express and arguments to back it up. Note that page 106 'Unsafe at any speed' can be used as an example of essay structure, as it is based on the five-point plan.

Differentiation: Less confident learners could write directly on the sheet, as this will support them in structuring their writing. More confident learners should write on paper and could be encouraged to add more paragraphs – for example, they could add and develop a third point.

Back at school: Ask volunteers to read out what they have written and discuss them further, both in terms of the points made and the way the writing is structured.

Page 111 Excel scientific instruments – Core skills

Objective: To interrogate texts to deepen and clarify understanding and response.

Setting the homework: Explain that most of the words we know have been learned by inferring (figuring out) their meanings from the context (the situation in which we hear or read the words). We should have the confidence to continue learning words in this way. Explain to the children that if they read the text carefully, they will find that most of the difficult words are explained.

Back at school: Definitions are one thing, but for the children to really understand these words, it will help to see photographs of the actual instruments. If possible, make suitable reference books or CD-ROMs available.

Page 112 Big and little – Core skills

Objective: To use knowledge of phonics, morphology and etymology to spell new and unfamiliar words.

Setting the homework: Go over the explanation of diminutives and explain the task. It is also worth pointing out that the normal form of the word is sometimes different from the diminutive – such as the normal form of *kitten* is not *kit*, but *cat*!

Differentiation: Some of the diminutives are not in common use, so all children, especially less confident learners, should be encouraged to look up words that they do not know.

Back at school: Display the page and invite the children to match the pairs. Highlight the suffixes used and ask children if they can think of any other diminutives using those suffixes.

Page 113 Baby bank – Core skills
Objective: To use knowledge of phonics, morphology and etymology to spell new and unfamiliar words.
Setting the homework: Explain to the children that a compound word is made up of two other words – for example, *skateboard* and *toothache*. Breaking compound words up into their two words will help with spelling. Encourage children to find existing compounds and invent new ones.
Differentiation: Knowing when a compound word should be two separate words, a hyphenated word or a single word is difficult, but less confident learners should not worry about this.
Back at school: Discuss which existing compound words were found and which new words were made up. Have fun sharing the invented dictionary definitions. A further follow-up would be to investigate the use of the hyphen in compound words.

Page 114 Dreadful language – Core skills
Objective: To use knowledge of phonics, morphology and etymology to spell new and unfamiliar words.
Setting the homework: Use the explanation to discuss some of the difficulties in English spelling. Reassure the children that some words are tricky, but they just have to be learned.
Differentiation: This basic work on spelling will benefit all children.
Back at school: Share other words with the same letter strings as those in the poem.

Page 115 Make it complex – Core skills
Objective: To use adverbs and connectives to establish cohesion within paragraphs and to clarify meaning and point of view by using varied sentence structure.
Setting the homework: Revise the main ways of connecting points. Read through the explanations and examples with the class.
Differentiation: All children should be able to use the first three methods. More confident learners can also try the phrase in apposition. The final method is the most challenging.
Back at school: Experiment with complex sentences in the context of a piece of writing. For example, the children could be asked to write half a page on one of the following topics:
- Describe being part of a large crowd at an exciting event
- Write a scene for a ghost story
- Write an argument for or against one of the following: Christmas is too commercialised; All British police should carry a gun.

Poetry – Unit 1 Creating images

Page 116 See, saw, stegosaur
Poetry objective: To read and respond to poems that use similes.
Setting the homework: Revise the term 'simile' using the example in the first verse. Explain how to write about similes using the example. Saying why a simile is effective is not always easy, but it is important as it helps children to understand what the writer is trying to say.
Differentiation: Use the first task only for simple reinforcement of the term 'simile'. Use both tasks to teach the more difficult process of writing about similes.
Back at school: Discuss children's explanations of the similes in the poem. Apply this knowledge to the study of another poem and write about similes, along with other aspects of the poem such as subject, verse form and personal response. Ask for children's responses to the question: *What is the tiny mammal in the last verse?* (A human, perhaps?)
Link to *100 Literacy Framework Lessons Y4*: PU1, Phase 1, Day 2: identifying similes.

Page 117 Seeing colours
Poetry objective: To explore and create similes.
Setting the homework: Children should already know what a simile is before being set this homework. Draw attention to the importance of using the punctuation correctly when reading the poem, or the sense of it will be lost.
Differentiation: Some children may need their helper to read the poem for them.
Back at school: As a class, identify the similes. Ask some children to read their own similes, missing out the name of the colour for the rest of the class to identify.
Link to *100 Literacy Framework Lessons Y4*: PU1, Phase 1, Day 2: identifying similes; Phase 2, Day 1: creating similes.

Page 118 A poem cube

Poetry objective: To write a poem using similes and other devices to create imagery.
Setting the homework: It is a good idea to make up your own poem cube to show the children what the finished product will look like. Tell them that each sentence should start with the noun that they are writing about: *eyes, teeth, feet, roar* and so on. This task will be easier if the sheet is enlarged to A3.
Back at school: Children can share their poem cubes, reading the similes for others to identify the animal from the clues in their simile sentences. Read some examples for the whole class.
Link to *100 Literacy Framework Lessons Y4*: PU1, Phase 2, Day 1: creating similes.

Page 119 Poem v poem

Poetry objective: To discuss poems and identify distinctive features.
Setting the homework: If possible, enlarge the page to A3 to allow space for writing. Revise the terminology used – *rhymed verse, free verse, rhythm, simile, metaphor.*
Differentiation: For less confident learners, simplify the frame and ask only one question in each section.
Back at school: Discuss the similarities and differences between these poems. Use the template as a guide to reworking the ideas into essay form as a whole-class activity.

Page 120 Mandy's studio – Core skills

Objective: To revise the use of commas in a list; to use varied sentence structure.
Setting the homework: Go over the explanation emphasising that these three punctuation marks are often used together to punctuate complex lists. Draw children's attention to the pattern.
Differentiation: Children who cannot write simple lists using commas and *and* should write three separate sentences with simple lists to describe each area of the studio. More confident learners could experiment by writing the items in a different order, then choosing the one that sounds best.
Back at school: Ask volunteers to write their lists on the board and others to comment on how accurately they have been punctuated.

Page 121 New word generator – Core skills

Objective: To use knowledge of word structures and origins to develop their understanding of word meanings.
Setting the homework: Many new words draw on a common fund of prefixes, roots and suffixes, some of them very ancient. Many new words are based on whole existing words. They become the root of the new word. Explain to the children that the task involves using their imagination to invent some exciting and useful new words.
Differentiation: This activity is accessible to all, though less confident learners may need help with the meanings of some of the roots, prefixes and suffixes.
Back at school: Discuss the new words and what they mean. Create a piece of shared writing using these words.

Poetry – Unit 2 Exploring form

Page 122 Lots of legs

Poetry objective: To discuss vocabulary, structure and language features used to create effects in poetry.
Setting the homework: Revise the term 'rhyme': words ending with the same sound. Explain how to annotate rhyme schemes using letters of the alphabet, 'a' for the first rhyme, 'b' for the second and so on. Couplets are annotated 'a a, b b' and so on.
Differentiation: The task can be made easier for less confident learners by filling in either all the rhymes or all the riddles (names of horror creatures), so that they can concentrate on one thing.
Back at school: Go over the rhymes and the riddles and ask the children to try to write similar rhyming couplets. They could add more verses to this 'Ghoulography' or they could choose another subject, such as animals or countries. Answers to the riddles are: *alien, ghost, mummy, ogre, troll, unicorn, yeti.*

Page 123 The creature of Croglin

Poetry objective: To discuss vocabulary, structure and language features used to create effects in poetry.

Setting the homework: Revise the term 'rhyme': words ending with the same sound. Explain how to annotate rhyme schemes using letters of the alphabet, 'a' for the first rhyme, 'b' for the second and so on. Alternate rhymes are annotated 'a b a b' and so on. Ask children to practise reading the poem aloud. Explain that they should ignore the lines, but follow the punctuation – for example, not: *...eyes that seemed to creep* (pause) *towards her,* but *...eyes that seemed to creep towards her* (pause).

Differentiation: Sheets for less confident learners could have some of the rhymes written in. The rhymes are as follows: *hall, shriek, sleep, light, door, floor, light, gun.* More confident learners could write a continuation referred to in the second task.

Back at school: Discuss the rhymes and ideas for continuation. If any children have written continuations they could be read out.

Page 124 Whale

Poetry objective: To write a poem using a form already explored.

Setting the homework: Revise the terms 'adjective', 'verb', 'phrase', 'adverb' and 'simile' and explain that knowledge of these will be necessary when following the prompts in the table.

Differentiation: Less confident learners, and those who have difficulty understanding any of the above terms, should keep referring back to the model poem. More confident learners should depart from the model and develop their poem in any way they wish.

Back at school: Share the poems written and discuss ways in which they can be further developed.

Page 125 Haiku

Poetry objective: To read and respond to poems in different forms.

Setting the homework: Reading and writing haiku is a very good way to get into syllable counting as the haiku form depends entirely on syllables, not on rhythm or rhyme. Explain that the homework is a simulation of the skills required to write haiku – count syllables, and express an idea in a set number of syllables.

Differentiation: Less confident learners could practise counting syllables before doing the homework. More confident learners could write haiku of their own.

Back at school: Go over the syllable count for each line and discuss ways of correcting lines that are too long or too short. Follow up immediately with reading some more examples of haiku and by children writing their own.

Link to *100 Literacy Framework Lessons Y4*: PU2, Phase 1, Day 1: work on haikus.

Page 126 From aqua to aquarium – Core skills

Objective: To use knowledge of word structures and origins to develop their understanding of word meanings.

Setting the homework: Explain that all these root words are from Latin, which has had a great influence on the development of English. Encourage the children to study the cards before cutting them up.

Differentiation: More confident learners could match the extra words to the roots. Some may be able to find other words that have come from these Latin roots.

Back at school: Check the homework as a whole-class activity. Additional Latin roots you might suggest children find modern words for are: *circum (round)* and *manus (hand).*

Page 127 Number prefixes – Core skills

Objective: To use knowledge of word structures and origins to develop their understanding of word meanings.

Setting the homework: Check that the children understand the word prefix. Explain that when they think they have found a suitable word they must ask themselves whether it suggests a number. This will enable them to reject words that begin with the same letters but are not number prefixes such as *biology* and *bite.*

Differentiation: Less confident learners could work with 'uni-', 'bi-', 'tri-' only. More confident learners could tackle the extension task.

Back at school: Read out and discuss the words and make a class list of words with number prefixes. Add to this during the term.

NARRATIVE

Name	Date

Character quotes

■ Choose one of the main characters from a story you are reading and describe the character with evidence from the text. Use the table below to help you.

Description of characteristics Describe the following characteristics in your own words.	**Evidence from text** Quote words, phrases or sentences as evidence for your description. Enclose in quotation marks.
Appearance	
Personality	
Relationship with others	
Important actions	

Illustrations © Garry Davies.

Dear helper
Objective: To identify the main characteristics of characters, drawing on the text to justify views.
Task: Ask your child to describe the character to you and, as they do so, help them identify which aspect of the left-hand column it belongs in. Encourage them to find something to say for each aspect. Then help your child to look through the story to find quotable evidence to support their description.

NARRATIVE

Name	Date

Into the shelter again!

● Read the text below, and underline all the words and phrases that give you clues that the story is set in the past.

The sirens went off again in the middle of the night. Mr Lace shouted "Are you awake Joan? Come on girl, wrap up warm – and don't forget your gas mask."

I wasn't taking any chances – I knew how cold it was in that shelter so I grabbed my eiderdown as well as my dressing gown. Mrs Lace had one tiny torch so that we could see our way across the garden through the blackout. She shouldn't have had it really, but we'd never have found our way in the pitch black, and hurrying as well. And she did keep it pointing down to the ground.

"Watch you don't tread on my veg!" warned Mr Lace, laughing. "I'm digging for victory, remember!"

This was the second night on the trot that the German planes had flown over. We didn't expect a raid, but it was always best to be careful and follow the air raid precautions that we all knew about. Mrs Lace did her best for us, and tried to have some food ready in the shelter, even though the rations didn't go very far.

I felt lucky to have been evacuated to the Lace's. Some of my school chums weren't quite so happy though. Jimmy Johnson cried a lot and kept writing letters back home to his mum, asking her to come and take him home.

We knew we were in a safer place, here in the countryside, but it didn't always feel like that when we heard those Messerschmidt engines overhead. We would listen to them and wonder which city might get bombed tonight. Maybe the pilots didn't know where they were since all the signposts had been taken down!

Illustrations © Garry Davies.

Dear helper
Objective: To identify vocabulary that indicates that a story is set at a particular time in the past.
Task: Encourage your child to read as much of the text as they can on their own, but help with words they find difficult. They should be able to identify the time in which the story is set, but ask them to tell you which words and phrases gave them the clues. See if they can explain or describe these key words.

NARRATIVE

Name _____ Date _____

Powerful verbs

◼ Replace the highlighted verbs with powerful ones to make the writing more interesting and informative. Write your new verbs on the lines. You can choose from those in the box, but if you have better ones, use your own ideas.

seemed	arrived	yelled	move	explained
grinned	shuffled	asked	replied	
appeared	mumbled	noticed		spotted

The new children

Mr Gardner, our teacher, told us about them before they

(**came**) _____. He (**said**) _____ that it

would be hard for the new children because they had to leave their homes

and families and (**come**) _____ to a place they didn't know.

We'd (**seen**) _____ some of them before they came to

school, of course, as they were living near us in the village. But on that first

day they (**walked**) _____ slowly into the playground. Some

of them were shy, some were worried and some were angry. One boy

(**shouted**) _____ "Stop staring at us!" He was right, we were

staring, so Tom went up to them and (**said**) _____ "Do you

want to play It?", and the angry boy (**smiled**) _____ a bit

and (**said**) _____ "All right then."

Dear helper
Objective: To use more powerful verbs to improve a piece of writing.
Task: Read through the piece with your child before discussing the best replacements for the highlighted verbs. There are more verbs in the box than you will need, so ask your child to choose the one they think works best, or use one of their own. Ask them to re-read the completed piece to be sure they are happy with their choices.

Name _____   Date _____

A character from the past

● Create your own character to fit in with your chosen historical setting. Draw them in the centre of the page and write information about them in the boxes.

The name of my character is _____

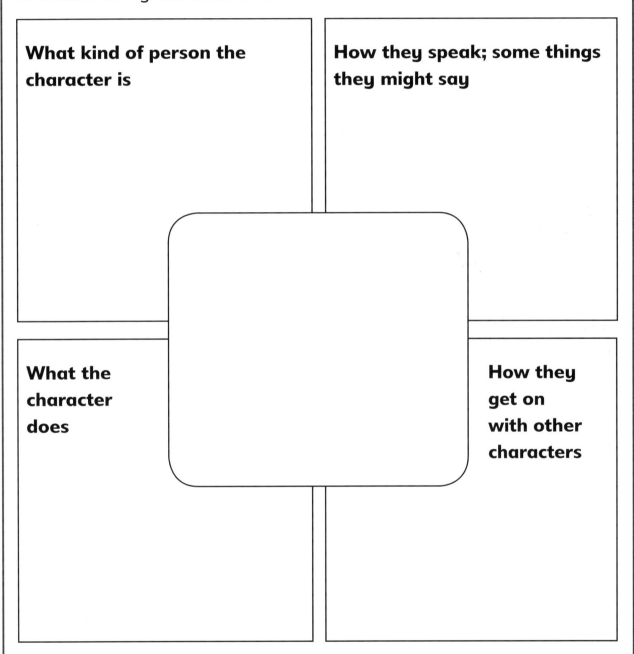

What kind of person the character is

How they speak; some things they might say

What the character does

How they get on with other characters

Dear helper
Objective: To create a character to fit in with a particular historical setting.
Task: Your child will know the historical setting for their character. Talk with them about the kind of character that would work well in their setting and period of history, sharing ideas about the kinds of things they might write in the boxes to help develop the character.

NARRATIVE

Name   Date

Out of time

Viking	Ancient Egyptian woman	Knight
Cave man	Ghost	Medieval monk
Castaway	Ancient Greek children	Victorians

Illustrations © Garry Davies.

■ Think of settings in which you might find these characters.

■ Choose one or two characters and think of different or unusual settings in which they might be placed.

■ Make notes about how the characters would behave differently in these unusual settings. Use a separate sheet.

Dear helper

Objective: To use a historical setting as a starting point for creating a new story.

Task: Help your child to explore how different settings would affect different characters. For example, if a caveman was in a garden, he might pick the crops for himself, not realising they belonged to someone, or if a medieval monk was in a palace, he might feel shy and be unable to speak to anyone.

What do you like to read?

◼ Read these blurbs from actual books, and say which you would like to read, and why.

> Good evening, brave reader! But are you brave enough to join Polly and Friday as they climb Goblin Mountain to battle the forces of evil? For be warned. This book is full of swords and trolls and witches and a thing that looks like a gherkin. And somehow that old roo-de-lally Mr Gum is all mixed up in it too. Shabba me whiskers, it's a burpin' epic!
>
> *from* Mr Gum and the Goblins *by Andy Stanton*

> A secret gateway to a magical island, a lost prince, a wizard, an ogre, a fey and a hag make this a fun, fantastic fairy tale.
>
> *from* The Secret of Platform 13 *by Eva Ibbotson*

> Living in a supermarket deepfreeze wasn't very nice for the tiny doll, until one day a very special little girl came along, and thought of ways to make her happier.
>
> *from* The Little Girl and the Tiny Doll *by Edward and Aingelda Ardizzone*

> There has been a terrible mistake and Wayside School has been built all wrong! The classrooms were meant to be in a row and now they are on top of each other. Maybe that is why strange things happen at Wayside School.
>
> *from* Sideways Stories from Wayside School *by Louis Sachar*

I would choose _____

because _____

_____

Dear helper
Objective: To use book blurbs as a guide to choosing new books to read.
Task: Talk about the possible content and style of the books described, and discuss how they might appeal to your child, and why. If they would choose more than one, they can continue on the back of the sheet.

Name _____ Date _____

A wet blanket

◾ Do you know or can you guess the meanings of these common expressions? The first one has been done for you.

◾ Add any other expressions that you know to the table and write down their meanings.

A wet blanket

a discouraging person

At a loose end

_____

Get into hot water

_____

Lead a dog's life

_____

_____

Sit on the fence

_____

_____

Pull a leg

_____

_____

Common expression	Meaning

Illustrations © Theresa Tibbets/Beehive Illustration.

Dear helper
Objective: To investigate common expressions.
Task: Many expressions that are well known to adults are a mystery to children! Encourage your child to guess any meanings that they don't know before you tell them. Help them to think of and define others.

PHOTOCOPIABLE ◾SCHOLASTIC
www.scholastic.co.uk

Name   Date

Archaic words

◾ Investigate these archaic words by highlighting in different colours:

  ❑ words for jobs that no longer exist;

  ❑ words for things that are no longer used;

  ❑ words for things that still exist, but which have been replaced by a new word.

◾ You may find a dictionary helpful.

Archaic word	Meaning
arseling-pole	a pole used by bakers to move hot ashes
bakester	a female baker
beadle	a keeper of an alms house or prison
cockler	a seller of cockles
colic	a cough or cold
farrier	a blacksmith
fortepiano	a piano
gramophone	a record player
ice chest	used to keep food cool before refrigerators
keel-alley	a bowling alley
kissing-comfits	sugar plums (used to sweeten the breath)
magic lantern	an early type of projector
moonling	a lunatic
ostler	a stableman at an inn
pantry	a room in which food is stored
parlour	the best room in the house
phonograph	the earliest type of recording machine
radiogram	a record player and radio combined
stenographer	a person who writes shorthand
telegraph	sends messages in morse code
topless	excellent
ugsome	ugly
wireless	radio
yammer	cry loudly
zoetrope	a toy that displays moving pictures

Illustrations © Garry Davies.

Dear helper

Objective: To understand that vocabulary changes over time.

Task: Read and enjoy this list of archaic words with your child, then help them to investigate it, by highlighting different kinds of words in different colours. Can you think of any more archaic words that your child can add to the list? Remind your child to look out for old words and expressions in their reading.

Name _____ Date _____

Prefix it!

Prefix cards

auto	trans	tele	bi	circum
circum	auto	trans	tele	bi
bi	circum	auto	trans	tele
tele	bi	circum	auto	trans

Root cards

graph	mit	scope	cycle	vent
ference	ography	parent	vision	plane
ceps	navigate	mobile	port	pathy
phone	sect	stance	matic	plant

■ Cut out the cards. Keep them in two separate packs (**roots** and **prefixes**).

■ Shuffle each pack to mix up the cards and then place them face down.

■ Pick up one card from each pack. Try to match a prefix to a root card.

■ Score one point for matching the cards and one point for saying what the word means. Use a dictionary to check. Score a bonus point for spelling the word when the cards have been turned over.

Illustrations © Phil Garner.

Dear helper

Objective: To find out about the meanings and spellings of words with the prefixes: 'auto', 'bi', 'trans', 'tele', 'circum'.

Task: Remind your child that a root is the basic part of a word to which letters (a prefix) can be added to the beginning to change its meaning. Play the game with your child following the rules. Encourage your child to look up words in a dictionary, learn their meanings and practise their spellings.

PHOTOCOPIABLE ■ SCHOLASTIC
www.scholastic.co.uk

Name	Date

Alice

◼ In this extract from *Alice in Wonderland*, underline the parts of the text that show how Alice reacts to the setting she is in. Look for things she thought, how she felt and things she did.

There were doors all round the hall, but they were all locked; and when Alice had been all the way down one side and up the other, trying every door, she walked sadly down the middle, wondering how she was ever to get out again.

Suddenly she came upon a little three-legged table, all made of solid glass; there was nothing on it except a tiny golden key, and Alice's first thought was that it might belong to one of the doors of the hall; but, alas! either the locks were too large, or the key was too small, but at any rate it would not open any of them. However, on the second time round, she came upon a low curtain she had not noticed before, and behind it was a little door about fifteen inches high: she tried the little golden key in the lock, and to her great delight it fitted!

Alice opened the door and found that it led into a small passage, not much larger than a rat-hole: she knelt down and looked along the passage into the loveliest garden you ever saw. How she longed to get out of that dark hall, and wander about among those beds of bright flowers and those cool fountains, but she could not even get her head though the doorway; 'and even if my head would go through,' thought poor Alice, 'it would be of very little use without my shoulders. Oh, how I wish I could shut up like a telescope! I think I could, if I only know how to begin.' For, you see, so many out-of-the-way things had happened lately, that Alice had begun to think that very few things indeed were really impossible.

from Alice in Wonderland *by Lewis Carroll*

Illustrations © Garry Davies.

Dear helper
Objective: To find evidence in a text that shows how a character behaves in a particular setting.
Task: Help your child to read the passage and look together for phrases that show how Alice reacted to being in this unusual setting.

NARRATIVE

Name _____ Date _____

Creating an atmosphere

■ In the text below, identify and highlight the details the writer has used to create atmosphere.

The Sultan's palace

The carpet flew through the night sky, like a silent comet, giving the boy a distant view of misty hills. Moonlight occasionally caught the golden-domed towers of the city below, as he expertly guided his craft to a gently swooping landing in the courtyard of the Sultan's palace. Sounds were few – the breathing of a large dog somewhere nearby; insects chirruping in the trees overhead; wind-chimes tinkling in the breeze.

Which way should he go? The carpet looked safe enough there in the shadows, where its bright colours were indistinguishable from the flowered grass in the gloom of the night. The boy looked all about him as he walked carefully towards the nearest arched doorway. A faint light could just be seen glimmering from a room somewhere inside. It seemed to be beckoning to him. He was expecting a light – a light to show him the way. Was this the right one? There was only one way to find out, so he continued on his quest, his senses alert, watching, listening, waiting for danger.

He could hear a faint trickling of water, as though in a small fountain. The delicate perfume of jasmine blossom met his nostrils. This seemed to be a magical place. The light he had seen began to grow stronger; as though it was greeting him. Sitting next to the lamp he could now make out the shape of a person – a slim girl seated cross-legged on a large silken cushion. She seemed to be waiting for something – or someone.

Illustrations © Garry Davies.

Dear helper
Objective: To identify details used by writers to create atmosphere.
Task: Help your child to read the passage through, before talking about the sections where the writer has chosen words and images to create atmosphere. Look for how language has been used, the structure of sentences and the use of punctuation and paragraphing.

PHOTOCOPIABLE **◾SCHOLASTIC**
www.scholastic.co.uk

Name   Date

Alien planet

 Alien planet	 Desert island	 Land of giants
 Haunted house	 Medieval castle	 Magic mountain
 Space station	 Dragon island	 Undersea world

◖ Choose one of the cards above as a setting for a story. Look at the scene carefully, then develop it in note form by:

◻ thinking of adjectives and figures of speech to describe it

◻ drawing a map of the area (on a separate page)

◻ adding place names

◻ adding details, especially those that could be used in a story, such as a deep well.

Dear helper
Objective: To develop use of settings in their own writing.
Task: Discuss the card that your child chooses, helping them to add imaginary details.

NARRATIVE

Name   Date

Imaginary worlds

Crumbling cave	Deep dark forest	Dragon	Dwarves' mine
Elixir of life	Fortress of doom	Goblin	Imprisoned princess
Magic mirror	Murky mire	Mysterious museum	Prince's palace
Treasure chest	Wicked wizard	Witch	Witch's hovel

Cut out the small pictures above and paste them on a sheet of paper to create a map of a fantasy world. Add larger details such as roads, rivers, mountain ranges and so on. Add your own ideas.

Illustrations © Garry Davies.

Dear helper
Objective: To understand how writers create imaginary worlds.
Task: Discuss each picture and how it could be used on a map. Note that some of the cards, such as the treasure chest, can be used as motives for a story line and the creatures can be used as hazards. As the map takes shape, discuss possible stories that could grow out of it, and work out detailed descriptions of places, people and objects.

PHOTOCOPIABLE **SCHOLASTIC**

www.scholastic.co.uk

Name	Date

Dinosaur Plateau

■ Plan a story based on this map. Your adventure should start in Porto Paso. Your quest is to get to Dinosaur Plateau and bring back some dinosaur eggs or baby dinosaurs which are worth a small fortune.

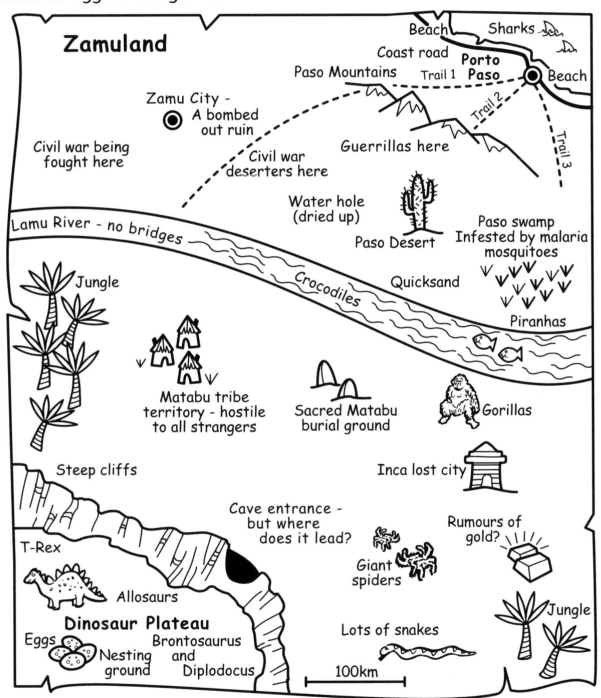

Illustrations © Garry Davies.

Dear helper

Objective: To use different ways of planning stories.

Task: Discuss the map with your child, and the kind of adventures that explorers would have if they tried to get to the plateau. Help your child to make a paragraph plan, in which each paragraph describes a stage of the journey, an adventure or an incident.

NARRATIVE

Name   Date

Dragon slayer

■ Decide which of the sentences in this passage to join with connectives to make it more interesting for the reader. Where you want to join sentences, cross out the full stops and write your chosen connective above them.

■ Show where you would start a new paragraph by marking the place with two lines like this: //

The fearsome dragon had been terrifying the townsfolk for years. They knew where he lived. Some of them had tried to fight him. None of them had succeeded. They lived in terror. The king decided to try to find someone brave enough and clever enough to finally get rid of the dragon. He sent out a proclamation across the land. Posters went up everywhere. On a bright but chilly morning a small young man arrived in the town. "I have come to fight your dragon," he announced. The people laughed. "You!" they jeered. "You are too young, and too tiny!" The boy took no notice. "Where will I find your king?" he asked. The people showed him the way. "I have come to fight your dragon," he told the king. "Are you sure you are up to this challenge? You look very young," said the king. "Don't worry your highness," replied the boy. "Trust me. I know about dragons. I live in a land where there are many dragons. Before I go, I need to know three things. What colour is your dragon? How old is it? Is it male or female? This information is important. It will help me make my plan. There is more than one way to catch a dragon."

Illustrations © Garry Davies.

Name	Date

Monty Mouse

Rules for writing paragraphs

In stories, a new paragraph is shown by an indentation of approximately 1cm from the margin. Start a new paragraph for each big step forward in the plot.

■ Use the rules above and the paragraph plan below to help you to write a story in paragraphs. Use a separate piece of paper.

Monty Mouse lived happily in Grandma's house...
☐ Describe Monty, his comfortable mouse hole, and how he lived.

One day, he looked out of his mouse hole and saw – a cat!
☐ Describe the cat that Grandma has just bought and how Monty feels about it.

Things went from bad to worse when...
☐ Describe how the cat nearly caught him. This paragraph should have lots of exciting description.

Monty realised that he would have to get rid of that cat, so he sat down to think up a plan...
☐ Explain Monty's plan.

The day came when his plan was going to be put into action...
☐ Describe how the plan works. This paragraph is the climax of the story. It should be full of excitement. The reader should be kept in suspense until the last moment about whether the plan will work.

Peace at last...
☐ End the story by describing how Monty settles happily into his old routine.

Illustrations © Garry Davies.

Dear helper
Objective: To use paragraphs in story writing.
Task: When your child is writing the story, help them by checking that they are following the rules of paragraphing correctly.

Pirate talk

- Highlight all the synonyms of **said** in this passage adapted from *Peter Pan*.
- On a separate sheet, list the synonyms and add any others you can think of.

Michael began to cry, and even John could only speak in gulps, for they knew Hook's reputation.

"He was Blackbeard's bo'sun," John whispered. "He is the worst of them all."

"That's him," moaned Peter.

"What is he like? Is he big?" enquired John.

"He is not so big as he was," boasted Peter.

"How do you mean?"

"I cut off a bit of him."

"You!" guffawed John in disbelief.

"Yes, me," declared Peter sharply.

"I wasn't meaning to be disrespectful," apologised John.

"Oh, all right," said Peter in a forgiving tone.

"But, I say, what bit?" questioned John eagerly.

"His right hand," announced Peter.

"Then he can't fight now?"

"Oh, can't he just!"

"Left-hander?"

"He has an iron hook instead of a right hand, and he claws with it," stated Peter grimly.

- Re-read the passage, using different synonyms. You could write each of your new synonyms above the word in the text.

Illustrations © Theresa Tibbets/Beehive illustration.

Dear helper
Objective: To collect synonyms that will be useful in writing dialogue.
Task: Remind your child that a synonym is a word with a similar meaning to another. Help your child to identify the synonyms of *said* in the passage and to think of new ones. Check that the new ones are appropriate as you re-read the text together, replacing the synonyms.

Illustrations © Garry Davies.

Name _____   Date _____

Quickly

An **adverb** describes a verb. Many, though not all, adverbs are made by adding **-ly** to adjectives. In the sentence 'She ran quickly', the adverb **quickly** tells us how she ran.

■ Add a different adverb to each of the following sentences.

Mr James ran _____.

He drove _____.

It rained _____.

The car stopped _____.

She laughed _____.

Jim answered _____.

The music played _____.

The girl sighed _____.

Jake did his homework _____.

Time passed _____.

■ Underline the adverbs in *Escape*.

Tip: Look for words ending in **-ly**.

Escape

He ran quickly down the street. He looked anxiously left and right. Fortunately everything was quiet. He felt tired and rather unhappy to be running away so soon. He reached the crossroads and stopped momentarily. He started again and turned cautiously into the High Street. Suddenly he stopped. There was the sound of footsteps behind him. His heart beat violently. He was being followed!

Dear helper
Objective: To identify common adverbs with '-ly' endings.
Task: Go over the explanation with your child. Help them to think of suitable adverbs for the sentences and to look for adverbs in *Escape*. Try reading the paragraph without the adverbs. Talk about how the adverbs help to improve the description.

Name _____ Date _____

Adverb attack

■ Choose a suitable **adverb** from this list to use in the sentences below. Example: "What a surprise!" said Sarah **excitedly**.

angrily	childishly	frostily	nervously	snappily
apologetically	coolly	grumpily	politely	softly
bluntly	crossly	hesitantly	proudly	spitefully
boastfully	deceitfully	hopefully	quietly	sulkily
brightly	eagerly	icily	sadly	sweetly
calmly	enthusiastically	loudly	scornfully	tactfully
cheekily	excitedly	miserably	sharply	wisely
cheerfully	frankly	moodily	shyly	wittily

"I'm not talking to you!" said Sally _____.

"I've just got to level 10 on that new computer game!" said Tim _____.

"My boyfriend has just finished with me," said Zoe _____.

"I'm not taking any notice of you," said the schoolboy _____.

"Perhaps it will stop raining," said the tour guide _____.

"Shhh! You'll wake the baby," said Mum _____.

"Well, how are we feeling today?" said the nurse _____.

"You look like you slept under a bus," said Ashra _____.

Extension

■ Choose three other **adverbs** from the list and use them in sentences of your own. Write them on the back of the sheet.

 Remember: Use adverbs to improve dialogue in your own writing!

Dear helper
Objective: To use adverbs effectively when writing dialogue.
Task: Remind your child that adverbs can tell us how a person is thinking or feeling when they say something. Read the adverbs and discuss in what situations they would be used. Encourage your child to think carefully when choosing the adverbs.

PHOTOCOPIABLE ■SCHOLASTIC
www.scholastic.co.uk

Name _____ Date _____

Punctuation posers

A **comma** is used to mark off a **subordinate clause** when it begins the sentence. Example:

main clause:

Cinderella changed back into a kitchen maid

subordinate clause:

when the clock struck twelve.

subordinate clause:

When the clock struck twelve,

main clause:

Cinderella changed back into a kitchen maid.

■ Rewrite these sentences, on the back of this sheet putting the **subordinate clause** at the beginning and marking it off with a comma.

Tip: Find the **connective** and move it with the following clause to the beginning of the sentence.

Prince Charming was the favourite of the ladies because he was rich and handsome.

Buttons loved Cinderella although he was too shy to tell her.

The three sisters went to the ball while Cinderella cleaned out the fireplace.

Cinderella saw her fairy godmother when she looked up.

You will marry a prince even though you are poor.

Your coach will change back into a pumpkin unless you leave by midnight.

The three sisters were unkind to Cinderella because they were jealous of her.

I shall keep looking until I find the foot that fits this glass slipper.

Illustrations © Phil Garner.

Dear helper

Objective: To use punctuation marks accurately in complex sentences.

Task: The hardest part of this homework is finding the subordinate clause. Find the connective, then move it with the following clause to the beginning of the sentence. This list of connectives will help you and your child: *although, because, though, unless, until, when, while.*

All in a good clause

A **main clause** makes sense on its own and contains a verb.
Example: Zoe **played** a tune on her saxophone.

A **subordinate clause** does not make sense on its own.
Example: A difficult piece of music.

■ Read each of these clauses and ask yourself:
Does it contain a verb? Does it make sense on
its own? Put a tick (✓) next to the main clauses.

The portrait was beautifully painted. ☐

A new and very powerful computer. ☐

I enjoy watching television. ☐

Spreading destruction everywhere. ☐

Chloe hoped to write a bestselling novel. ☐

A difficult piece of homework. ☐

Taken completely by surprise. ☐

Tim enjoys playing snooker. ☐

By a strong wind. ☐

My new puppy made a mess on the carpet. ☐

Illustrations © Phil Garner.

Dear helper
Objective: To identify main clauses.
Task: Remind your child that main clauses make sense on their own, but that subordinate clauses
depend on main clauses for their sense.

PHOTOCOPIABLE ◼SCHOLASTIC
www.scholastic.co.uk

Name	Date

Fanso and Granny-Flo

◼ In the extract below, underline any words or phrases that let you know this story is set in a different country.

All the villagers had a big open worry – the drought that was on. For days it seemed it would rain, but the rain did not come.

The lands were cracked open and brittle. Food-crop leaves went into a deeper brown colour. Drought sucked the whole island dry. Grass in Jamaica was brown. Through all districts, the terrible dry-time had turned rivers, streams and ponds into near mud-holes, trampled by hooves and human feet. Then, with rain merely hanging about, the air was impossibly hot and stifling.

Granny-Flo and Fanso were at work in their backyard. Surrounded by clusters of banana trees, scattered coconut-palms and spaces of white heat haze, they worked outside the kitchen doorway. They usually worked here, in the shade of the kitchen and the ackee tree, when their job was like today's. They shelled coconuts, milled them and boiled the milk into oil. Like many other district people, they produced their coconut-oil both for market and home use.

So, hair freshly plaited, bare arms with silver bangles, feet sandaled, and wearing an old blouse and long skirt, a piece of brown sugarbag sacking for apron, Granny-Flo sat breaking coconuts and pulling out the pieces.

Her blunt stumpy machete came down hard on a coconut gripped in her left hand. Cracking it, then opening it, she then let the coconut-water drain from the hollow inside into a bucket. With her strong slender knife she skilfully prised the white coconut kernel from its shell. Faster than Fanso could pick them up and mill them, she piled up the white pieces.

From *A Thief in the Village and Other Stories* by James Berry

Text © 1987, James Berry.

Dear helper
Objective: To identify the language that describes a story setting.
Task: Read through the passage with your child to get a feel for it before discussing the particular elements of the story that let the reader know about the setting.

NARRATIVE

X35

Name	Date

Story research

■ Think about the story you have been sharing at school which is set in another country. What extra information can you find out about the country? Answer as many of the questions as you can. You could use books, travel brochures, an atlas or the internet, or ask people you know.

The country I am finding out about is _____

Which continent is the country in? _____

What language (or languages) are spoken there? _____

_____

What is the money called? _____

What is the capital city? _____

If the country has a coastline, what sea or ocean is it next to? _____

_____

What rivers or lakes are there? _____

_____

Are there any mountains, and what are they called? _____

_____

What are the main religions of the country? _____ _____

What kinds of food are eaten? _____

_____

Is the country well known for anything, such as a famous building or event, or particular crops or products? _____

_____

Dear helper
Objective: To research the country in which a story is set.
Task: Help your child to find as much of the above information as possible. If they use the internet they will need some help and supervision when using a search engine.

Name	Date

Banja's coming of age

■ Read the extract below then discuss the following:
- ☐ What skills has Banja been taught that help him to survive?
- ☐ What are the 'coming of age' tests in Western European society?
- ☐ How would you cope if you were in the same situation as Banja?

■ Write your ideas on the back of the page.

This extract describes Banja's coming of age – he has to pass a test before he can be accepted as an adult. The test is to walk across 100 miles of desert, navigating by the stars and surviving on the food and water he can find on the way.

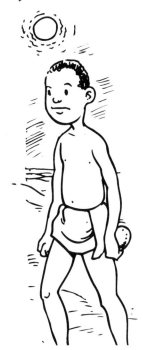

Banja was worried. He had been walking all day through the burning desert. He knew that he should have reached Nonang Wadi by now, but there was no sign of it. Banja belonged to the Kung people. He was short and wiry in build, like all his people, and this helped him to bear the great heat of the desert. He had also been taught many survival skills – and now he found that he needed them.

He had taken his last drink of water two hours ago and his water carrier, a huge ostrich eggshell, was empty. As he walked, his eyes swept the ground. He was looking for a hollow in the sand – especially one where the sand appeared slightly darker. At last he found one. He knelt and took a hollow reed from his skin bag. Then he pushed the reed gently into the sand and blew through it. This was to clear out any sand which had clogged the end of the reed. Then he sucked gently. He coughed – sand! He tried again in a different spot, and this time he sucked water. He filled his mouth, rinsed the water around, and swallowed. The next time he filled his mouth, he did not swallow the water, but spurted it out again into the ostrich eggshell. He managed to do this several times before the water ran out and he sucked sand again.

Banja stood up and smiled. He knew now that he would survive. All he had to do was work out where he had gone wrong, and he could do that when the star patterns appeared again at night.

From *Banja's Coming of Age* by Jie Nalikwanda

Extension

■ Write a continuation of the story. Use a separate piece of paper.

Illustrations © Garry Davies.

NARRATIVE

Name _____ Date _____

Character interview

◀ Choose one of the main characters from the story you have been working on at school. Write some questions that you could ask them, to find out more about them. You might want to know more about their background, how they feel about other characters in the story, what they think about some of the main events, and what they think might happen next. Use the back of the sheet if you need more space.

Character's name: _____

Question 1: _____

Answer: _____

_____

Question 2: _____

Answer: _____

_____

Question 3: _____

Answer: _____

_____

Question 4: _____

Answer: _____

_____

Dear helper
Objective: To devise questions to ask a character from a known story.
Task: Ask your child to tell you about the story and help them to select a character. Talk with them about how they might phrase the questions before they write them down.

Name

Date

In the hot-seat

◼ You will need the questions you devised for your chosen character in the story you have been reading at school. Give them to your helper, who will ask you the questions. You will be in the 'hot-seat', and should answer as though you were the character. Afterwards, write some of the answers you gave in the space below. When you read it back, it should sound like the person talking about themselves.

Character's name _____

Question 1: _____

Answer: _____

_____

Question 2: _____

Answer: _____

_____

Question 3: _____

Answer: _____

_____

Question 4: _____

Answer: _____

_____

Dear helper
Objective: To work in role in order to find out more about a character in a known story.
Task: Use your child's questions and encourage them to give as full answers as possible – you may need to prompt them by asking *Why was that?* or *What else can you say about that?* Their writing does not have to include everything they said if they gave very detailed answers.

Crocodile river

■ Fill the gaps in the passage below with the most powerful verb you can think of. For example, in the first gap, **feared** would be more powerful than **knew**.

In this extract from Nigerian Noon, *Sulu must pass a test of courage so that he can become a warrior. The test is to swim across a river full of crocodiles.*

The river was wide and brown after the rains. Sulu could see no crocodiles, but he _____ they were there. He _____ down the river bank and began to swim. He _____ his feet as hard as he could and _____ with his arms, but he hardly seemed to move. In his mind he _____ crocodiles _____ towards him. He wanted to scream and _____. He wanted to _____, but he knew that he would fail the test and be _____ back to his mother instead of the warrior's kraal* with the other men.

Then he _____ a long grey shape in the river. It _____ towards him at great speed. He took a deep breath and _____ to the bottom of the river where he stayed until his lungs felt like they would _____. When he surfaced, the grey shape had _____.

Sulu _____ on until the other bank seemed nearer. He was now so exhausted that he hardly cared if a crocodile _____ him or not. At last he reached the bank and was helped out by a band of young warriors. They clapped their hands and _____. "You are now a man and a warrior!" they _____. "Come with us to our kraal."

* kraal: a large hut woven from dried reeds

Sulu finds out later that there are no crocodiles in that part of the river. Swimming across, believing the river to be full of crocodiles, was the test of courage. The 'grey shape' was a log.

Illustrations © Garry Davies.

Dear helper
Objective: To use powerful verbs effectively in a story.
Task: The most effective form of help is to read through the passage with your child and help them to make sense of the gaps. For example, the second gap needs a verb for how Sulu went down the river bank, such as *slid* or *clambered*.

Name	Date

Jason's flying saucer

Object cards

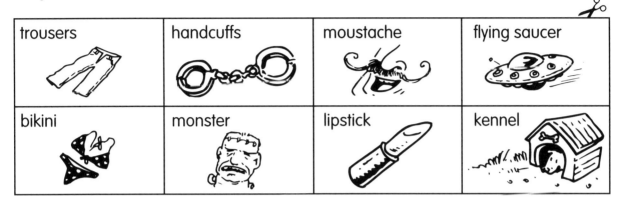

| trousers | handcuffs | moustache | flying saucer |
| bikini | monster | lipstick | kennel |

Owner cards

| Jason | The policeman | Mr Smith | The alien |
| Susan | Dr Frankenstein | Mrs Green | Rover |

The **possessive apostrophe** is used to show ownership.

Example: Rover's mobile phone was attached to his collar.

◼ Play the 'Apostrophe game'. Here's how:

☐ Cut out the cards and put them into two sets, **object** and **owner**.

☐ Shuffle each set and place them face down.

☐ One player chooses a card from each set and gives them to the other player.

☐ The other player has to write out a sentence like the example above using the words on the cards. If it is written correctly, they win a point.

☐ The players take turns. The player with the most points at the end is the winner.

Dear helper

Objective: To use the apostrophe accurately to mark possession.

Task: Play the 'Apostrophe game' with your child. Check that they write full sentences that begin with a capital letter, use the apostrophe correctly and have a full stop at the end.

Name   Date

Phantom phrases

◼ Fill each gap in the passage below with one of the following phrases or clauses. Add a comma before and after the phrase or clause (unless it comes at the end of a sentence).

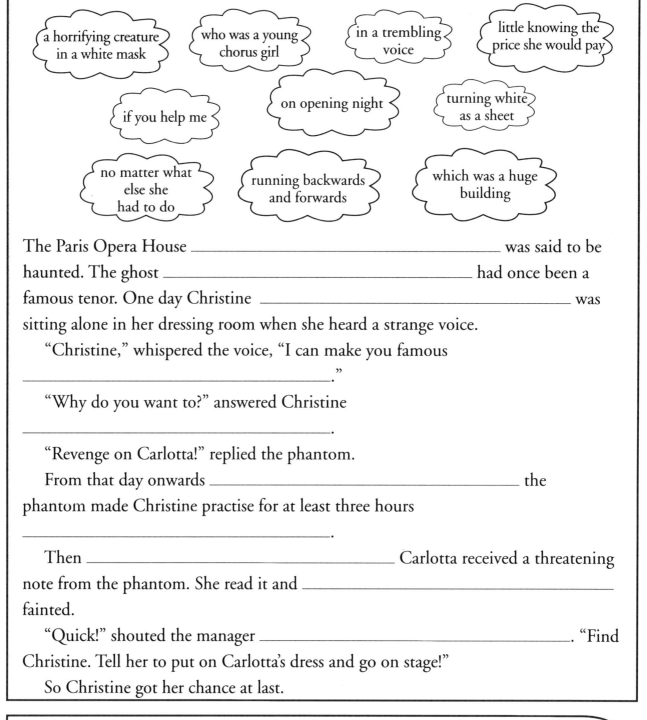

a horrifying creature in a white mask

who was a young chorus girl

in a trembling voice

little knowing the price she would pay

if you help me

on opening night

turning white as a sheet

no matter what else she had to do

running backwards and forwards

which was a huge building

The Paris Opera House _____ was said to be haunted. The ghost _____ had once been a famous tenor. One day Christine _____ was sitting alone in her dressing room when she heard a strange voice.

"Christine," whispered the voice, "I can make you famous _____."

"Why do you want to?" answered Christine _____.

"Revenge on Carlotta!" replied the phantom.

From that day onwards _____ the phantom made Christine practise for at least three hours _____.

Then _____ Carlotta received a threatening note from the phantom. She read it and _____ fainted.

"Quick!" shouted the manager _____. "Find Christine. Tell her to put on Carlotta's dress and go on stage!"

So Christine got her chance at last.

Dear helper
Objective: To use commas when adding phrases and clauses to sentences.
Task: Your child should be learning how punctuation helps the reader make sense of complex sentences. This will help their reading and writing. Read the story with your child and discuss which phrases fit in which gap. Check that they have used a comma before and after each clause or phrase.

Whose is it?

Apostrophes can be used with common and proper nouns to show possession.

Rule 1:   If the noun is singular, add an **apostrophe** and an **s**.
Example: **John's gold, the teacher's pet, James's horse, the ass's tail**.

Rule 2:   If the noun is plural and doesn't end in **s**, add an **apostrophe** and an **s**.
Example: **the children's toys, the men's waistcoats**.

Rule 3:   If the noun is plural and ends in **s**, add an **apostrophe** but no **s**.
Example: **the smugglers' cave, the dogs' bones**.

◀ Rewrite these sentences using apostrophes.

The passengers ticket is no longer valid.

The headmistresss office door was firmly closed.

Janes socks do not match.

Mr Rosss class performed a nativity play in assembly.

The mices hole can be seen just by the front door.

I shivered when the doctors stethoscope touched my back.

The womens race was won by an international athlete.

Texass oil rigs dominate the landscape.

All the gardeners plants were ruined by the rain.

Illustrations © Phil Garner.

Dear helper
Objective: To revise use of the apostrophe to show possession.
Task: Discuss how the use of apostrophes helps us to see what belongs to who. The last sentence is a tricky one. Ask your child: *Is* gardeners *singular or plural?*

NARRATIVE

Name   Date

Bina's betrothal

As you read this story extract, think about what Bina's problem is.

'I have found just the boy for your Bina,' said Mami (Mami is the Tamil name for matchmaker).

Mother looked pleased. 'Oh that sounds very good! Tell me, what is the young man's name?'

'Balraj. It is a good name for a man. It means mighty and powerful.'

'And how old is he?'

'Twenty-four.'

Mother frowned. 'But Bina is still only fifteen!'

Mami laughed. 'True, she is young by the standards of this country, but of course, in India she would probably be betrothed already – possibly even married!'

At that moment the front door slammed.

'Is that you, Bina?' called Mother. 'Come here, I have some good news for you.'

Bina walked slowly into the room, her head hanging. Her mother's good news usually meant something unpleasant – like last year's holiday in Tamil Nadu when she had wanted to go to Disney World in Florida.

'Bina,' said her mother breathlessly. 'You know Mami. She has found you a good match – a young man called Balraj.'

'What?' shrieked Bina. 'I don't want an arranged marriage! When – if – I marry, I want to choose my own husband. I want to marry for love!'

Mami looked at Mother. Both were deeply shocked.

from Bina's Betrothal by Nadeen Naik

Discuss the problem: Should Bina follow the traditional customs of her family's culture, or should she follow her heart? Write your ideas on the back of this sheet.

Extension

Mami and Mother have more nasty surprises in store. Bina already has an English boyfriend, whom she has been seeing in secret. Write an episode about what happens when Mami and Mother find out.

Illustrations © Garry Davies.

Dear helper
Objective: To identify social, moral or cultural issues in a story.
Task: Discuss the issues raised by this extract. Ask: *What is Bina's dilemma? What problems will she face if she goes against her community?*

PHOTOCOPIABLE ■SCHOLASTIC
www.scholastic.co.uk

Name	Date

Lost wallet

◼ Read the story, then:
- ❑ discuss the boys' dilemma (a dilemma is a difficult choice)
- ❑ explain the problem and alternative courses of action
- ❑ plan an ending for the story based on what you think they should do.

The bus slowed down and stopped. It was the stop before school. One man got off, but Balraj and Ben hardly noticed him, until they realised that he had left something behind – a wallet. Balraj picked it up and shouted after the man, but it was too late. The bus had already started again.

He sat back down and Ben said, "Here, let's have a look." Balraj passed over the wallet, and Ben opened it. "Hey, there's a five-pound note here!" he said.

"You're not thinking of keeping it?" said Balraj.

"Why not?" said Ben. "Finders keepers."

"It's not worth being dishonest just for five pounds," said Balraj. "You could earn that quickly just by mowing Granny Smith's lawn!"

"What if it were £1000?" said Ben.

"Er…" Balraj hesitated, "Well, I suppose it's still the same! You'd better give that wallet to me and I'll hand it in."

Balraj took the wallet and looked through it. "Look, here's his address," he said after a moment, "and…what's this?"

He took out a folded piece of paper. He unfolded it and spread it out between them. It was a roughly sketched map. The main city on the map was Porto Paso in South America and there was a dotted line to a place marked with compass bearings. Somebody had scribbled near the bearings: 'Inca gold here.'

"It's a treasure map!" exclaimed Ben. "That settles it. We keep the wallet and the map and go and find the treasure. We'll be rich!"

"Find the treasure – what with?" said Balraj. "Do you know how much a ticket to South America will cost?"

"I'll save up for it!"

"Yeah, for about ten years! I think this map makes it even more important to give the wallet back."

Illustrations © Garry Davies.

Dear helper
Objective: To write critically about a dilemma raised in a story.
Task: Discuss the situation with your child. Speculate about what might happen as a result of alternative courses of action. What are the moral issues?

NARRATIVE

Name	Date

The best words

■ For each of the situations below, write words or phrases that you might use when writing a story about it. Think of characters' thoughts and feelings. You might write the words they say or think, or what someone else might say to them.

Someone has to give bad news to a friend.

_____

_____

_____

Someone has to decide whether to admit to having told a lie, because someone else is being accused in their place.

_____

_____

_____

Someone has to make an important journey but a severe weather warning has been issued.

_____

_____

_____

A bully has offered someone money to steal sweets from a shop.

_____

_____

_____

Dear helper
Objective: To choose suitable words to use in writing a story with a dilemma.
Task: Only key words and phrases are needed here – not a whole story. Discuss possible words that might be used to describe emotions, thoughts and ideas, trying to think of different words for each situation. The word *worried* might be appropriate for each character, but try to find some alternatives. A thesaurus might be helpful.

Name   Date

Death by water

● Read the story and then discuss these questions:
  ☐ Do you believe that it is possible to see the future?
  ☐ What would you do if you were Phillipe?

"Take off your clothes," ordered Nostradamus.

"What, all of them?" said Phillipe.

"You came to have your fortune told, didn't you?"

"Yes, but I thought you would read my palm."

Nostradamus laughed. "What do you think I am – some old gypsy woman? I am the greatest fortune-teller in France! I read the whole body, not just the palm – look!"

He pointed to a chart on the wall. It showed the front and back of a man with dots all over him so that he looked as though he had the measles. Each dot was labelled.

"I can read the stars of the body, just as easily as the stars in the sky," said Nostradamus.

"What are the stars of the body?" asked Phillipe.

"Why moles of course! I can read them more easily than you can read a book!"

"I can't read," said Phillipe.

"Umph," said Nostradamus as he began a very thorough examination of Phillipe's moles. Phillipe blushed, and wished he would hurry up, but he seemed to take an age.

At last Nostradamus stood up straight. "You will be rich and famous and live to a ripe old age," he said, "but only if you follow the fate written on your body."

"What is that?" said Phillipe.

"You must join the army and become a soldier. Soon you will work your way up to be a general – the most famous that France has known. But beware of water. I see death by water if you are not careful."

Phillipe hung his head.

"What is the problem, boy?" asked Nostradamus. "I have told you that you will be rich and famous."

"I wanted to be a sailor," said Phillipe.

Either

● Write a paragraph about whether you think it is possible to see into the future.

or

● Plan a continuation of the story which proves the fortune-teller right or wrong. Use the back of this page.

Illustrations © Garry Davies.

Dear helper
Objective: To write critically about a dilemma raised in a story.
Task: Discuss with your child the questions raised at the top of the page. Then help your child to choose one of the writing activities and work with them to plan their writing.

NARRATIVE

Name   Date

What do you think?

■ For each of the situations below, think about how the characters might react to the dilemmas they face, and talk about the different things they might do. Choose one short story to prepare for retelling to a partner.

1. Mrs Smith, an elderly pensioner, is walking along the street when she finds a purse with money and credit cards in it. There is also a name and address on a card inside the purse.
   What might she do?

2. Adam has agreed to meet his friend to play football on Saturday afternoon. He then receives an invitation to go to another friend's swimming pool party, which is at the same time.
   What might he do?

3. Billy the Bully keeps taking some of Kaylee's packed lunch every day at school. He warns her that if she tells, he will wait outside school for her and beat her up.
   What should she do?

4. When Diego's teacher asked who had been to Australia, he was the only one who put up his hand. Everyone was very impressed, and asked him to bring in his photographs to show them. But Diego had lied – he hadn't actually been to Australia.
   What can he do now?

5. As Sammy skidded into the parking area on her bike, she crashed into another child's brand new mountain bike, denting part of it and knocking the mirror off. No one saw the accident happen.
   What will she do?

6. It's nearly Christmas, and Jana and Lukas had discovered where their parents were hiding their Christmas presents. They were very excited and dying to know what they were going to get for Christmas.
   What might they do?

Dear helper
Objective: To consider situations where characters must make decisions when faced with a dilemma.
Task: Ask your child to suggest possible actions the characters might take, explaining why they might choose to do each of them. Discuss what would be the best or right thing in each situation. Help them to develop one scenario to describe to a partner back at school. They could make brief notes on the back of this sheet to act as a prompt.

PHOTOCOPIABLE ■SCHOLASTIC

www.scholastic.co.uk

Name _____ Date _____

My advice is...

From a book you know well (perhaps one you have been reading in school), or from a TV programme that you watch, choose a character who has a problem to solve or a difficult decision to make. Imagine they have asked you, as another character in the story, to help them decide what to do. In the space below, write a letter to the character, telling them what you think is the best course of action, and explaining why.

Dear _____   _____

_____

_____

_____

_____

_____

_____

_____

_____

_____

_____

_____

_____

_____

_____

_____

Illustrations © Garry Davies.

Dear helper
Objective: To write in role, advising a character how to deal with a problem.
Task: When your child has selected the character, talk with them about the problem the character faces, and discuss possible advice that might help them. Which character will they be, giving the advice? They should try to write as though they were that particular person, thinking about what they might say, and how they might say it.

NARRATIVE

Name   Date

A good start

■ Some stories start by setting the scene, using well-chosen language to paint pictures with words. Using the information for each of the settings below, write an opening that will grab the reader's attention. Think about using adjectives, powerful verbs and adverbs as well as a mixture of short and longer sentences.

The setting is the countryside in winter. There is a lot of snow on the ground, there is a blizzard in progress, and one car is trying to drive along the icy road.

■ Write your story opening here:

The setting is a factory on fire. Fire-fighters are trying to put out the fire. It is very windy. Some people are watching. The face of a person can be seen at an upstairs window.

■ Write your story opening here:

Illustrations © Garry Davies.

Dear helper
Objective: To write a good story opening, using well-chosen vocabulary.
Task: Openings like *One day...* and *Once upon a time...* should be avoided. Tell your child to imagine they are telling someone about the scene as it happens and to dive straight into the story. Encourage them to think carefully about their word choices.

Name   Date

Alternative endings

■ In 'Goldilocks and the Three Bears', Goldilocks runs away when she is discovered, and we never find out what the bears did afterwards. What might have happened if the girl had stayed to face the bear family, and what might they have done, faced with the dilemma of having an intruder in their home, who had created havoc? Write an alternative ending to the story, starting when the bears find Goldilocks in Baby Bear's bed.

Illustrations © Garry Davies.

Dear helper
Objective: To write an alternative ending to a known story.
Task: Discuss with your child the various things that might happen in this scenario. What might the bears decide to do, and what might be the consequences for Goldilocks?

Name   Date

I see the sea

Homophones are words that sound the same but have different meanings and spellings: *homo* (same) + *phone* (sound). They are the cause of many mistakes!

see (to look)   **allowed** (to have permission)

sea (body of water)   **aloud** (noisily)

Sometimes, there are three alternative meanings:

there (a place)   **their** (belonging to them)

they're (short for 'they are')

◼ Circle the correct homophone from the words in brackets. If in doubt, check in a dictionary.

She looked for (**there, their, they're**) coats.

We went to (**buy, by**) some sweets.

It is (**to, too, two**) hot.

She (**through, threw**) the ball.

It went (**through, threw**) the window.

She settled down to (**right, write**) the letter.

I (**hear, here**) the noise.

We hoped the (**weather, whether**) would change.

She told a good (**tail, tale**).

She began the letter, '(**Dear, Deer**) Sir'.

Extension

◼ There are five mistakes in the paragraph below. Find them and rewrite the paragraph correctly in the box.

Jake past the ball to Stella, but she missed it. Anwar caught it and through it to Handa. Unfortunately, it went write passed her into the neighbour's garden, braking the window.

Illustrations © Garry Davies.

Dear helper
Objective: To learn the spelling and meaning of words that sound the same but are spelled differently.
Task: It is worth pointing out that homophones have a valuable purpose: the different spellings help to avoid confusion about meaning. However, there's no easy rule for spelling. The words just have to be learned!

PHOTOCOPIABLE ◾SCHOLASTIC
www.scholastic.co.uk

Name   Date

Fussy werewolf

An **adjective** is a describing word. It describes the noun it goes with.

Examples: The horse pulls a **heavy** load.

The **gruesome** creature kissed me.

That mountain is **high**.

◀ Fill the gaps in the passage below with suitable **adjectives**.

The werewolf climbed in through the _____ window.

He saw a _____ cot where a _____ baby was

sleeping. He bared his _____ teeth in a _____

snarl and crept towards the cot. He paused to look at the baby. She had

_____ hair, her eyes were _____, and she

was wearing a _____ sleep suit and a _____

nappy. Suddenly, the werewolf noticed a _____ smell. The

baby's nappy needed changing! "Yuck!" grunted the werewolf, "I prefer

_____ food!"

Illustrations © Garry Davies.

Dear helper
Objective: To revise adjectives.
Task: Help your child to fill the gaps in the passage by checking to see that each one is an adjective.

Name _____   Date _____

A sitting duck

- Try to explain these common sayings and clichés.

- Add two more sayings and their explanations to the list.

Saying	Explanation
a sitting duck	
a square meal	
hit the nail on the head	
bury the hatchet	
blow your own trumpet	
let sleeping dogs lie	
the writing is on the wall	
under the weather	

Illustrations © Phil Garner.

Dear helper
Objective: To collect and explain a range of sayings and clichés.
Task: These sayings are often well known to adults, but less so to children. Help your child to understand each saying by describing a situation in which it might be used. Help your child to think of other sayings.

PHOTOCOPIABLE ■SCHOLASTIC
www.scholastic.co.uk

Add an adverb

■ Read the list of **verbs** and the **adverbs** that could go with them.

■ Add other suitable adverbs in the **Your adverb** column.

Verb	Adverb	Your adverb
acted	rashly	suddenly
answered	correctly	
decided	reluctantly	
explained	clearly	
listened	attentively	
ran	quickly	
sang	sweetly	
shone	brightly	
slept	soundly	
smiled	happily	
spoke	sadly	
thought	deeply	
trembled	nervously	
walked	slowly	

Extension

■ Write sentences using five of the verbs and adverbs. Use the back of the sheet.

Illustrations © Phil Garner.

Dear helper

Objective: To understand how adverbs can be used with verbs to make writing more descriptive.

Task: If necessary, remind your child that a verb is a word that names an action and an adverb is a word that describes a verb. Help your child by giving examples of situations in which the given verbs and adverbs might be used together. If they need help thinking of extra adverbs for column three, ask questions, such as: *If you were worried about something, how would you sleep?*

NARRATIVE

Name   Date

Improvisation

◾ Using the sheet 'What do you think?' choose two or three of the scenes to improvise (make up) what two characters might say to each other.

◾ Where only one character is mentioned in the outline, invent a second who could be involved in a conversation with them. You will need a helper to be one of the characters as you play out the scene.

◾ After your improvisation, choose one conversation to write down in the form of a playscript.

Title: _____

Cast: _____

_____

_____

Scene: _____

_____

_____

_____

_____

_____

_____

_____

_____

_____

_____

_____

Dear helper
Objective: To improvise a dialogue and write it as a playscript.
Task: Help your child by acting the role of one of the characters from the scenarios they have chosen. Remind them to use stage directions when they write the dialogue as a script.

PHOTOCOPIABLE ◖▮SCHOLASTIC
www.scholastic.co.uk

Name   Date

Goldilocks – the play

◢ Write the final scene for 'Goldilocks and the Three Bears', in the form of a playscript, using the alternative ending you devised earlier. Remember to include stage directions, and set the script out so that actors can easily follow it. When you have written it, perform it with your helper.

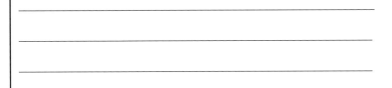

Illustrations © Garry Davies.

Dear helper
Objective: To rewrite a known story as a playscript.
Task: Ask your child to explain what they know about stage directions before they start to write. Help them to perform the play afterwards and discuss any ways it might be improved, making the changes as necessary.

NARRATIVE

Name	Date

Pantomime planner

◼ Use this planning page to give you some ideas for a modern pantomime. Write an outline for your pantomime on the back of this page.

Popular pantos

◼ Choose one of these popular pantomimes. You could also have fun by choosing more than one and mixing up the plots. For example, what would happen if Little Red Riding Hood found Sleeping Beauty in Grandma's bed?

- ☐ Aladdin
- ☐ Little Red Riding Hood
- ☐ Sleeping Beauty
- ☐ Cinderella
- ☐ Snow White
- ☐ Hansel and Gretel

Stereotype breakers

◼ Include one or more of the following to make your pantomime modern and different.

Characters

- ☐ A rapping prince
- ☐ A tough princess
- ☐ An alien
- ☐ A genetically modified plant

Settings

- ☐ A burger bar
- ☐ A football stadium
- ☐ Another planet
- ☐ A car factory

Objects

- ☐ A computer
- ☐ A mobile phone
- ☐ A sports car
- ☐ A guitar

Illustrations © Garry Davies.

Dear helper
Objective: To write a playscript using known stories as a basis.
Task: Help your child to remember the stories of the popular pantomimes, and then discuss how to make it modern and different. Use the ideas on the planner or some of their own.

PHOTOCOPIABLE ◼SCHOLASTIC

www.scholastic.co.uk

Name	Date

Toys alive!

◖ Read this playscript carefully, then practise it with your helper, ready for performing it with your friends back at school. You will need to take more than one part – how will you make the characters different when you read their words?

Scene: A child's bedroom at night. Toys are scattered around the floor, the child is asleep in bed.

Cuddly rabbit (*whispering quite loudly*): Psst! (*he pauses*) Psst! Is anyone else awake?

(*There is silence for a few seconds*)

Drag-along dog (*yawning*): Well, I was asleep. Dreaming about a juicy bone I was, 'til you started shouting all over the place.

Cuddly rabbit (*protesting*): I was not shouting! I know better than that!

Drag-along dog: Well, you're shouting now, my friend.

Dino dinosaur (*quietly, slowly and importantly*): Excuse me, but it is beginning to get rather noisy in here. We must take more care. We don't want to wake up The Child, now do we?

(*Rabbit and dog look down, embarrassed*)

Cuddly rabbit (*quietly and apologetically*): All right, I'm sorry. But I was rather excited. It is tonight, after all. We've been planning this for so long; I don't think you can blame me.

Dino dinosaur (*sighing*): Well, I suppose you're right, and after all, you are a very young rabbit. But - all the more reason to take care. (*Now sounding businesslike and organised*) Now then Dog, do you have the string?

Drag-along dog (*pleased with himself*): Yes Dino, I certainly do. I hid it carefully under The Child's bed. I'll fetch it.

Cuddly rabbit (*sarcastically*): Well – don't make too much noise, will you?

Dear helper
Objective: To practise reading a playscript, taking note of stage directions.
Task: Help your child to read the parts according to the stage directions, modelling for them if necessary. Take turns to read the script, until your child feels quite confident with each part.

Name   Date

Turn it down!

There are four types of sentence:

Statements: That music is too loud.
Questions: Is that music too loud?
Exclamations: What loud music!
Commands: Turn that music down!

Do not forget to use question and exclamation marks where necessary. (Commands end with exclamation marks if sharply spoken or shouted.)

◀ Complete the gaps in the tables. Note that you will sometimes have to change the words when you change the sentence type, particularly for the commands.

Statement	It is a fast car.
Question	
Exclamation	
Command	Find me a fast car!

Statement	
Question	Are you going to France for your holidays?
Exclamation	
Command	

Statement	The King Charles Spaniel is a well-behaved dog.
Question	
Exclamation	
Command	Be a good dog!

Statement	You've got a lot of homework.
Question	
Exclamation	
Command	

Illustrations © Garry Davies.

Dear helper
Objective: To understand how a sentence changes when a statement is made into a question, a question becomes a command, and so on.
Task: Help your child to complete the tables. Most help will be needed with filling in the command boxes.

PHOTOCOPIABLE ◣◣SCHOLASTIC
www.scholastic.co.uk

Name	Date

Sleeping Beauty

- Read this version of *Sleeping Beauty*.
- Choose the most suitable **synonym** in brackets and highlight or underline it.
- Explain to your helper why you chose each synonym.

Prince Charming was a (**good-looking/handsome/brave/charming**) young (**man/guy/youth/prince**). He heard that a (**cute/beautiful/nice/pretty**) princess was sleeping in (**an ancient/an old/an impregnable/a big**) castle and could only be woken with a kiss. The problem was that the castle was protected by a (**huge/prickly/thorny/big**) hedge. The hedge was so (**prickly/dangerous/high/perilous**) that many knights had died trying to climb it.

It was a (**horrible/nasty/fearsome/scary**) sight. The thorns were as big as (**daggers/kitchen knives/dragon's teeth/rulers**), and (**skeletons/corpses/dead bodies/cadavers**) hung from them. The air was filled with the (**stench/pong/smell/aroma**) of their rotting bodies.

But Prince Charming was not (**scared/deterred/put off/frightened**). He walked (**bravely/courageously/determinedly/quickly**) towards the hedge and, to his amazement, the thorns turned to (**beautiful/lovely/nice/pretty**) flowers. That was because the 100-year spell ended at that moment – even though the prince knew nothing about it.

He walked (**happily/eagerly/quickly/excitedly**) to the castle where he found everybody (**snoozing/sleeping/dozing/resting**). Then he found his way to Sleeping Beauty's tower. He had never seen anyone so (**nice/sweet/cute/lovely**). Her skin was as pale as (**milk/snow/paper/silk**) and her lips were as red as (**blood/roses/paint/lipstick**).

He kissed her and she awoke with a (**jerk/start/twitch/jump**).

"What time is it?" she said (**quietly/breathlessly/curiously/sleepily**).

"It's five and twenty past eight in the morning of March the first, 1492."

"Oh, dear," she (**moaned/sighed/groaned/complained**), "That's much too early." And she went back to sleep for another 100 years!

Illustrations © Phil Garner.

Dear helper
Objective: To explain the differences between words with similar meanings.
Task: Check that your child has a good reason for each synonym chosen and that it is not repetitive (*prickly* in both sentences 3 and 4), inappropriate (*guy*), or boring (*nice*).

Name	Date

NON-FICTION

Meet the deadline!

▪ Use these notes to write a newspaper article.

What? A circus on the school field – anyone can pay to see the show.

Why? To raise money; for children to learn circus skills.

When? Next week – 6.30pm each night, 2.30pm Saturday and Sunday.

How? Headteacher contacted circus after advert came into school.

Where? Oldville Primary School.

Who? Circus Valdini; Headteacher Mrs Craig.

Headline _____

Illustrations © Garry Davies.

Dear helper
Objective: To use notes to write a newspaper report.
Task: Ask your child to talk through their report before they start to write. Remind them to include all the information, perhaps making up one or two quotes to include.

Name	Date

Fact or opinion?

◼ In the article below, use one colour to underline the facts, and another to underline the opinions.

During the Second World War, thousands of British children were evacuated to the countryside, where it was thought they would be safer than if they stayed in the cities. The evacuation first took place in September 1939, just at the outbreak of war. Some children probably thought it would be a great adventure, whilst we know from letters written at the time, that others were worried and upset at being separated from their parents.

"I remember thinking that my mum and gran might get bombed," recalled Mrs Rosie Smithers, a wartime evacuee. "I was very scared. It seems a strange thing to say now, but we all thought every German person was very bad. They were probably thinking exactly the same things about us! After all, lots of soldiers were told they had to fight, and they couldn't argue – they didn't all volunteer."

A new job had to be created to help arrange accommodation for the evacuees – the Billeting Officer. Most people thought it was not an easy job. The Billeting Officer had to match the evacuees with foster families, who were not always very pleased to suddenly have unknown children living with them. Mr Bill Roberts, who was too old to fight in the war, kept a diary at the time. One entry read: *These two evacuees are pests. They must have been brought up with no manners at all, judging by their behaviour. I don't think I've even heard them say please or thank you once since they got here.* Mr Roberts might have been right, but it is more likely that the two children were so scared and worried, that good manners would probably be the last thing on their mind.

NON-FICTION

Dear helper
Objective: To identify fact from opinion in a recount text.
Task: If your child is struggling, point out key words for them such as *thought, probably* and *might* to indicate an opinion. Ask them to explain how they know that some parts are facts – where is the evidence?

📖 **SCHOLASTIC** **PHOTOCOPIABLE**
www.scholastic.co.uk
100 LITERACY HOMEWORK ACTIVITIES · YEAR 4   **77**

Name

Date

NON-FICTION

A loaded gun?

■ Read this article about smoking. Highlight **facts** in one colour and **opinions** in another.

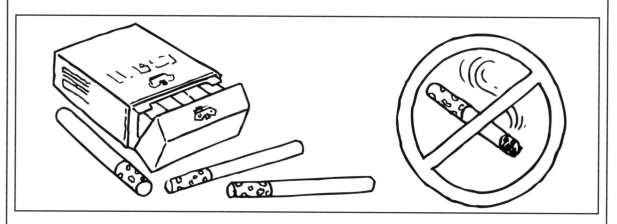

A loaded gun?

Cigarette smoking causes lung cancer. This has been proved by scientists. Smoking is a disgusting habit. Smokers' breaths smell foul and their clothes smell stale. Smoking was recently banned in all public places but I think tobacco should be made illegal – like drugs. After all, that is what tobacco is – a dangerous drug.

Scientific tests show that there are over 60 dangerous substances in tobacco smoke. Two of the most dangerous are carbon monoxide and tar. Carbon monoxide is a poison – it is the stuff that pours out of car exhaust pipes, and tar gums up the lungs.

Smoking by a pregnant woman increases the risks of miscarriage, low birth weight, and death of the newborn baby. We should therefore stop smokers for their own good. Tobacco is already highly taxed, but I think that the government should raise taxes so that nobody can afford tobacco.

The risk of dying from lung cancer is 20 to 30 times greater for a heavy smoker than for a non-smoker. So giving somebody a cigarette is like giving somebody a loaded gun and asking them to turn it on themselves and pull the trigger.

Illustrations © Garry Davies.

Dear helper
Objective: To distinguish between fact and opinion.
Task: Read the passage with your child, then ask them to highlight the facts first as they are easiest to find. Then, highlight statements that are clearly opinions. This will leave several statements left over that will have to be considered more carefully.

PHOTOCOPIABLE ■SCHOLASTIC

www.scholastic.co.uk

Name   Date

Newspaper features

◼ Use this chart to compare two newspapers.

	Name _____	Name _____
Layout and organisation Size of newspaper. How many columns? How many pictures per page? Use of colour? Type of font? Size of headlines and subheadings.		
Range of information What topics are included – for example, home news, world news, weather, finance, sport?		
Voice Who is writing? Which articles are anonymous? Which are by a named writer? Which are written by the editor? Which are written by advertisers?		
Formality Is the tone of the news paper friendly, formal (impersonal tone, big words, long sentences) or in between?		

Illustrations © Garry Davies.

NON-FICTION

Dear helper
Objective: To identify the main features of newspapers.
Task: Provide your child with two different newspapers (a broadsheet and a tabloid would be ideal). Discuss the features and look for examples in each of the papers.

Name   Date

NON-FICTION

Six honest men

Writer Rudyard Kipling wrote:

I keep six honest serving-men

(They taught me all I knew);

Their names are What and Why and When

And How and Where and Who.

■ These 'men' can be very helpful when writing news reports, as they can help us to make sure we have included as much information as possible. Try using them. Choose a recount in a newspaper, magazine or on a news website, and write notes about it under the 'names' of the 'men'.

Headline of article: _____

What? _____

_____

Why? _____

_____

When? _____

_____

How? _____

_____

Where? _____

_____

Who? _____

_____

Illustrations © Garry Davies.

Dear helper
Objective: To analyse a newspaper text, identifying key features.
Task: Help your child to choose a suitable article to use. They should make brief notes for each heading. Discuss which questions they find most evidence for.

PHOTOCOPIABLE ▪SCHOLASTIC

www.scholastic.co.uk

Name   Date

What's in the news?

- In the news article below, find examples of:

☐ Headlines ☐ Quotes ☐ Captions

☐ Use of the third person ☐ Use of the past tense

- Annotate the article, to show what you found and where they are. An example is given to help you.

BRAVE BEN MAKES IT AT LAST

Use of past tense →

Brave little Ben Brown has achieved his ambition to become a county swimming champion, despite a terrible accident that left him with his leg in plaster for three months.

"I'm so proud of him," said a happy Mrs Mary Brown, Ben's mother. "He has worked so hard and has always been determined that his accident would not hold him back. He's a star."

Ben Brown, our newest county swimming champion, proudly showing his medal.

Nine-year-old Ben was knocked off his bike six months ago, breaking his left leg in two places. A keen swimmer, Ben has never let the accident stop him from reaching his goal of winning a county championship. He has always been a talented swimmer, and has won many medals for his local club, The Sharks, so he carried out all the advice given him by doctors, including rest and exercise, in order to get back into competition.

Once the plaster was off, Ben worked doubly hard at his event, the front crawl, and now his hard work has been rewarded. Ben said, "I wasn't going to give up. I knew I'd got a lot to do, but it was the thought of that medal that kept me going."

Illustrations © Garry Davies.

Dear helper
Objective: To identify the features of a newspaper recount.
Task: There are more examples of the third person and the past tense than the other features, so encourage your child to find as many of them as they can. They should make their annotations neatly to avoid confusion.

NON-FICTION

Name	Date

The Giant's Grave

◾ First read the information below.

In the small town of Oldville, there is a legend that, hundreds of years ago, a treasure of some sort was buried deep inside the hill known as the Giant's Grave, just outside the town. Over the years many theories have been put forward about the name of the hill, with some people believing there really is a giant buried in there. However true that may be, the story about buried treasure is believed by most locals. Some think it is gold, others favour the idea of jewels, whilst a few think the treasure is the giant himself, complete with armour. Soon the truth will be known at last, as there is to be a major excavation of the site by local archaeologists.

◾ Now use the information to write a short article to fit the headline.

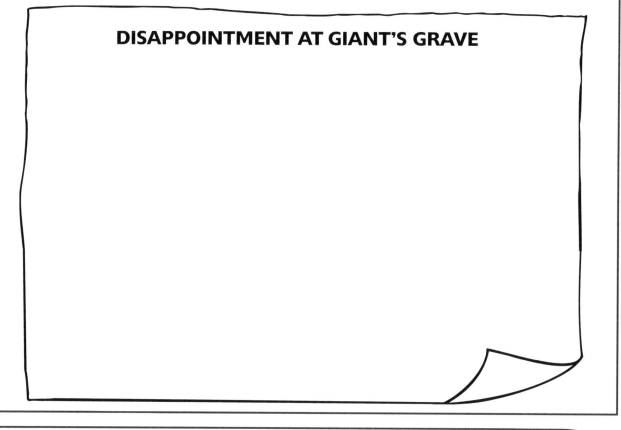

DISAPPOINTMENT AT GIANT'S GRAVE

Illustrations © Garry Davies.

Dear helper
Objective: To re-draft a recount into a newspaper article.
Task: Ask your child to tell you how a newspaper article is organised. Help them to use the information to write in a style that reads like an article in a newspaper, perhaps including some made-up quotes from locals or one of the archaeologists. Remind them their story must match the headline.

PHOTOCOPIABLE ◼◼SCHOLASTIC
www.scholastic.co.uk

Name	Date

Be a newspaper editor

◼ Your reporter has given you this rough draft of an article. It is nearly 300 words long, but you only have space for 150. Edit it down to size, and divide it into paragraphs. Use a separate page for your summary.

Suggestions:

☐ Leave out a whole section.

☐ Shorten each section as much as possible by including only essential information.

The expedition to Dinosaur Plateau returned yesterday. But it brings both good news and bad. The good news is that the dinosaurs do exist – in a way. The team found a new species of giant monitor lizard living on the plateau. The bad news is that giant monitor lizards may not be enough to attract tourists. Biologist Dr Paul Ricard, who is Professor of Biology at Panama University, described his first sight of the beasts. "We were hacking through the jungle with our machetes when I saw a huge scaly head rise above the undergrowth. At first I thought it was a real dinosaur, but when we got closer, I could tell that it was just a huge lizard." The scientific name for the monitor lizard is *Lacertilia Varanidae*. Monitor lizards like water, and are often found near lakes. They feed on eggs, fishes and molluscs. They lay eggs on dry land and can live for up to fifteen years. The largest species of monitor lizard in other parts of the world can grow to more than two metres in length. The monitor lizards on Dinosaur Plateau are nearly twice this size, and for this reason Dr Ricard named them *Lacertilia Varanidae Dinosauria*, which means Terrible Monitor Lizard. Another piece of bad news is that the lost Inca city is so badly ruined that it is just a pile of rubble. The government hopes that it will be possible to go ahead with tourist development anyway. They are pleased that Dr Ricard included the word *Dinosauria* in his new scientific name for the lizards, as they will be able to advertise the lizards as Dinosaur Lizards without breaking any laws.

Dear helper
Objective: To edit a newspaper story to fit a particular space.
Task: Read the rough draft of the article with your child and discuss what could be left out to make it fit the 150-word space.

CORE SKILLS

Verbalise it!

◢ Draw lines to show which **nouns** and **adjectives** have been changed into which verbs. The first one has been done as an example.

Nouns and adjectives	Verbs
bath	widen
circle	sharpen
cloth	moisturise
dark	obey
do	prove
drama	simplify
food	shorten
friend	grieve
frost	solidify
full	horrify
gold	freeze
grief	fill
horror	darken
life	strengthen
moisture	terrify
obedience	bathe
proof	do
sharp	befriend
short	live
simple	gild
solid	encircle
strong	clothe
terror	dramatise
wide	feed

Illustrations © Garry Davies.

◢ Can you see any patterns in the ways in which nouns and adjectives are made into verbs? Write them on the back of the page.

Dear helper
Objective: To investigate the ways in which nouns and adjectives can be made into verbs.
Task: Matching words is fairly easy. Your child will need most help when it comes to looking for patterns, such as the addition of '-ify'.

Got a nice garden

■ Rewrite each of these sentences with a different adjective in place of **nice-**

We have a nice garden. _____

What a nice day! _____

I'm reading a nice book. _____

I want to live in a nice house. _____

Mr Jones is a very nice man. _____

I'd like a nice cup of tea. _____

■ Rewrite each of these sentences with a different verb in place of **got**. Note that it is sometimes better to rewrite the whole sentence. For example, the first sentence could be rewritten as *Look at my Christmas presents!*

Look what I got for Christmas! _____

He got up at 7am. _____

Susan got a bad cold from her brother. _____

My computer's got a DVD drive. _____

Jason got to school just in time. _____

What have you got there? _____

Illustrations © Garry Davies.

Dear helper
Objective: To use alternative words to *got* and *nice*.
Task: It is important that children understand that there is nothing wrong with the words *nice* and *got* – they are perfectly correct English. However, they are overused. Help your child to think of alternative words. Note that, to avoid using *got*, sentences sometimes have to be reworded.

CORE SKILLS

Boy overboard!

In English, many words that sound the same are spelled differently to show different meanings. Words of this kind are called **homophones**. It is interesting to note dialect differences: **ant** and **aunt** are pronounced in the same way by Northerners, and **bomb** and **balm** are pronounced the same way by Americans!

◖ Read each sentence, then re-spell the words in italics so that they give the correct meaning. Write the re-spelled words in the space provided.

◖ Make up more humorous sentences of the same kind.

1. Throw that *boy* _____ overboard!

2. I enjoy watching *cereals* _____ on television.

3. There was a long *cue* _____ for snooker yesterday.

4. I would like a good quality bow made out of *you* _____.

5. I am sorry to tell you that she *dyed* _____ yesterday.

6. Are two burglars a pair of *knickers* _____?

7. Oh, I see that you've had your *hare* _____ done!

8. This *fir* _____ coat is very prickly.

9. I can't help until I get the *fax* _____.

10. London has elected a new *mare* _____.

Illustrations © Garry Davies.

Dear helper
Objective: To investigate links between meaning and spelling.
Task: Help your child to think of the correct alternative spelling for each word and to think of more sentences of the same kind. If they wish, they can draw cartoons to accompany their sentences.

Homophone cards

aisle	currant
faint	rain
gorilla	there
program	principle
board	die
grate	stair
serial	coarse
weather	profit
boy	eight
knight	practise
flour	blew
toe	bare

Set 1

buoy	ate
night	their
current	isle
reign	feint
bored	guerilla
principal	programme
dye	practice
stare	great
course	cereal
prophet	whether
blue	bear
tow	flower

Set 2

◼ Cut out the cards and play the game with a friend, parent or helper.

◼ Each player takes one set of cards. The first player puts down any card. The second player then has to find the matching **homophone** and define both homophones. If successful, that person wins a point.

◼ It is now the turn of the second player to put down a card and for the first person to find the matching homophone.

Dear helper
Objective: To distinguish between homophones (words with same pronunciation, but different spelling).
Task: Supervise while your child plays the game with another child. Alternatively, join in yourself.

Name	Date

Phantom pharaohs

■ Put the words from column 1 in alphabetical order in column 2 (the first two have been done as an example).

■ Give a simple definition in your own words in column 3.

Word	Arranged alphabetically	Simple definition
pie	phantom	A ghost
pheasant	pharaoh	The name for the ruler of Ancient Egypt
picture		
photograph		
pizza		
phoenix		
pig		
pharaoh		
pillar		
pile		
phobia		
phantom		
pigment		
pigeon		
phone		
picnic		
phrase		
piano		
physics		

Illustrations © Garry Davies.

Dear helper
Objective: To use second, third and fourth letters for alphabetical ordering and to define familiar vocabulary in own words.
Task: Your child can be helped with the first task by having a copy of the alphabet to which they can refer. For the second task, they may need help with the more difficult words. They may refer to a dictionary, but should be encouraged to re-state the definition in their own words.

NON-FICTION

Name	Date

The resort of the millennium

◾ Read this article, then find and underline examples of: **headings, lists, bullet points, captions**. You could use a different colour for each one.

◾ Discuss how these features help you to find information more easily.

Illustrations © Garry Davies.

PORTO PASO

Porto Paso is a city with a large harbour, and a good road leading along the coast to other major cities. It has wonderful weather all year round and some of the best beaches in the world, but at the moment, very few tourists go there. That is about to change.

Tourism

Porto Paso could be the tourist resort of the millennium. Among its advantages are:

- wonderful weather all year round
- some of the best beaches in the world
- near to a lost Inca city
- near to Dinosaur Plateau.

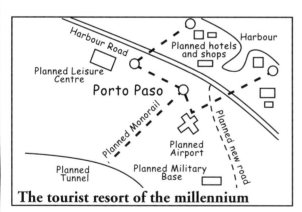

The tourist resort of the millennium

The Porto Paso development plan

2002 Develop the beaches and drive away the sharks.
2003 Explore Dinosaur Plateau and the lost Inca city.
2004 Build an airport at Porto Paso.
2006 Build a monorail to the Plateau and the Inca city.
2008 Build hotels, shops and restaurants for tourists.

Extinct? The government hopes not!

Dinosaurs

It is the dinosaurs that will bring the tourists flocking in. There are stories that dinosaurs have survived on a plateau about 400km to the south of Porto Paso. The government is planning an expedition to explore the plateau. If the reports are true, they expect that Porto Paso will be one of the richest cities in the world by the year 2010.

Holiday of a lifetime

Dear helper

Objective: To identify features of non-fiction texts: headings, lists, bullet points, captions.

Task: Help your child to find and underline the features listed above. Then, find a real magazine or newspaper, and look for the features there.

Name

Date

Porto Paso report

◾ Imagine that you are the chairperson of the Porto Paso development committee. The year is 2010, and you are writing your annual report based on the six headings below. Complete your report using these headings. The first has been done for you.

1. Develop the beaches and drive away the sharks.
    Toilets and restaurants have been built on North and South beaches, and a new bus service provided (until the monorail is finished). However, the shark control boats are finding it difficult to get rid of the sharks.

2. Explore Dinosaur Plateau and the lost Inca city.

3. Build an airport at Porto Paso.

4. Build a monorail to the Plateau and the lost Inca city.

5. Build hotels, shops and restaurants for tourists.

6. Will we be ready for 2010?

Illustrations © Garry Davies.

Dear helper
Objective: To write a report.
Task: Read *The resort of the millennium* with your child and discuss what problems might have come up that should be included in the report.

Name   Date

Non-fiction review

◀ After finishing a research task, evaluate some of the books you used by filling in this form.

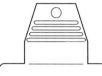

What I was looking for: Explain briefly what you wanted to find out.

Titles of books I looked at: List from two to four titles and say briefly what each was like (such as lots of text, few pictures, good index).

What I found out: Explain what you found out and note which book or books contained the most useful information.

How I found it: Explain the process of searching (looking at contents, scanning).

Which book was best and why: Give more detail about the good points of the book which you found most helpful.

Dear helper
Objective: To evaluate non-fiction books for their usefulness.
Task: Discuss the research task with your child, and ask them to talk about the different books. (These will already have been listed while at school.)

NON-FICTION

Name   Date

Flying machines

A **paragraph** is a series of sentences on one topic. Non-fiction paragraphs are sometimes introduced by **subheadings**. Non-fiction can be set out in indented or **block** paragraphs.

Indented paragraphs: new paragraphs are shown by indenting the first line by approximately 1cm.

Block paragraphs: new paragraphs are shown by leaving a whole blank line between paragraphs.

◀ Read the passage about flying machines and pick out four separate topics. Mark the beginning of each new paragraph with the symbol: //

◀ Think of a suitable subheading for each paragraph.

For centuries man has dreamed of being able to fly. As long ago as the 15th century, Leonardo da Vinci drew sketches of flying machines. However, he was ahead of his time and his machines were impossible to build with the tools of the day. Man's first successful flight took place in 1783. The Montgolfier brothers filled a large paper balloon with hot smoke from a fire, and it floated 1800 metres into the air. To the people watching, it seemed a miracle, but balloons and airships soon became common. The first flight by an aeroplane took place in 1903, at Kitty Hawk, in the USA. The aeroplane had been made by two brothers, Orville and Wilbur Wright. Though gliders had been flown successfully for many years, the importance of this invention was that it allowed for long-distance flight. The most exciting flight of all must be the journey to the moon. On 20 July, 1969, United States astronauts Neil Armstrong and Edwin Aldrin took off in one of the mighty Apollo rockets and travelled to the moon. They landed in the Sea of Tranquility. They did several experiments, and then took off for Earth with soil and rock samples. After a trouble-free flight, they landed safely.

Illustrations © Garry Davies.

Dear helper
Objective: To use paragraphs to organise information.
Task: Share the reading of the passage with your child. Careful reading will help them to decide when each new topic is introduced and, therefore, when a new paragraph is needed.

Name   Date

Legend or history?

- ◼ Read these notes about Robin Hood.
- ◼ Make notes about your own opinion in the blank oval.
- ◼ Use the notes as the basis for a short article. You can write it on a separate piece of paper.

Illustrations © Garry Davies.

Characters
- ❏ Little John – tall, named as a joke, Robin's right-hand man, grave can be seen in Hathersage, Derbyshire
- ❏ Friar Tuck – fat, merry – a holy man but a good fighter
- ❏ Allan A-dale – minstrel
- ❏ Maid Marian – Robin's ladylove – married at Edwinstowe church
- ❏ Sheriff of Nottingham – Robin's enemy, outlawed him, tried to get rid of him

Legend
- ❏ Robin Hood – an earl who was made an outlaw
- ❏ lived in Sherwood forest
- ❏ dressed in Lincoln green
- ❏ robbed from the rich, gave to the poor

Robin Hood

Legend or history?
My opinion

History
- ❏ Robin Hood mentioned in official documents for Yorkshire in 1230, as 'Robertus Hood, outlaw'
- ❏ Robin Hood mentioned in poem 'Piers Plowman' in 1377
- ❏ Gravestone at Kirklees Priory says 'Here lies Robard Hude'
- ❏ Lots of ballads – some from 14th and 15th centuries

Dear helper
Objective: To fill out notes into connected prose.
Task: Read through these notes with your child and discuss ideas for the empty oval. Help your child to turn them into connected prose, by checking that they are writing in full sentences.

NON-FICTION

CORE SKILLS

Only connect

● Read through this list of **connectives**, then try them out in an argument. Jot down any other useful connectives that arise during your discussion.

Additions

To give a reason:
because, for, the reason is

Additions

To add one idea to another:
also, another point, furthermore, in addition

Additions

To introduce an opposing idea:
but, however, on the contrary, on the other hand

Additions

To write about cause and effect and alternatives:
if… then, the result would be, either… or, neither… nor

Additions

To sum up a point:
on the whole, so we see that, therefore, to sum up, overall

Dear helper
Objective: To use connectives to structure an argument.
Task: Your child will have been given a topic or topics to discuss by the teacher. Discuss the topic with your child, pointing out any of the above connectives that come out naturally in discussion and adding new ones to the list.

Join it

Connectives are used to join different parts of a sentence together. Here are the ten most commonly used conjunctions:

although, and, as, because, but, for, until, when, where, while.

◼ Add an appropriate **connective** from the list above to join the clauses in each sentence.

1. He had completed his holiday plans _____ an unexpected problem arose.

2. There was a car in the garage _____ we couldn't use it because neither of us could drive.

3. People still talk about the haunting _____ it happened many years ago.

4. It was difficult to find the music shop _____ it was outside the main shopping centre.

5. Slowly the climber edged up the cliff _____ he managed to rescue the injured girl.

6. The weather was fine _____ we set out on our trip.

7. We stopped bailing out the water _____ it was just a waste of time.

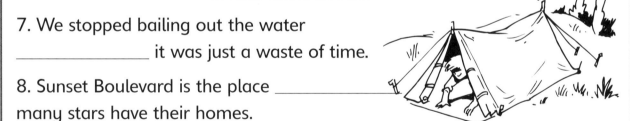

8. Sunset Boulevard is the place _____ many stars have their homes.

9. Tom put up the tent _____ Jerry got the camping stove going.

10. The champion started running at dawn _____ she didn't stop until she had beaten her record.

Illustrations © Phil Garner.

Dear helper
Objective: To use connectives to join clauses.
Task: Ask your child to read each sentence aloud and try different connectives until they find one that sounds right. More than one may be appropriate.

Name _____   Date _____

Using connectives

Connective cards
while
as
because
but
for
and
until
when
although
where

Statement cards
I like dogs.
I couldn't help laughing.
Jay dropped his ice cream.
The fire brigade worked hard.
Jo went on the roller coaster.
The crowd sheltered in the hall.
The fog grew thicker.
The fire was put out.
I don't like cats.
She drove slower and slower.
The rain poured down.
She was afraid of heights.

◼ Cut out the connective and statement cards and experiment with different ways of making complex sentences out of each pair of statements.

◼ Experiment with using connectives at the beginning of the sentence as well as in the middle and write down the best examples.

Extension

◼ Write six sentences that contain two statements linked by connectives.

Dear helper
Objective: To investigate connecting words and phrases.
Task: *Connective* is the term used to describe a word or phrase that connects sentences, phrases or other words. Your child should understand that the choice of connective can affect meaning.

PHOTOCOPIABLE ◼SCHOLASTIC
www.scholastic.co.uk

CORE SKILLS

Name	Date

Which is which?

The table below shows some of the features of three different text types: explanations, recounts and reports.

Explanations	Recounts	Reports
Explain a process or how something works	Retell events	Describe the way things are
Written in logical steps	Recount events in order but with added descriptive details	Don't have to have things in any particular order
Usually use present tense	Use past tense	Usually use present tense
Use connectives of time, and causes and effects	Use time connectives	Use connectives that make comparisons
Might have diagrams or illustrations	Might be letters, diaries, news reports	Might have tables, diagrams or illustrations
May use the 2nd person	Use 1st or 3rd person	Usually in the 3rd person

◼ For each of the summaries below, write in the box whether they are explanations, recounts or reports. Be prepared to explain your choices.

On the local TV news, an item telling you about the success of the local football team	
In a science book, a chapter about the water cycle	
A magazine article about how a farmer is changing the way he farms, so that he is producing organic crops	
A council leaflet, telling you how they recycle your rubbish	
An email from a friend, telling you about the holiday they have just been on	
An article comparing schools in three different countries	
An item on a radio programme, where a retired dustman is talking through memories of his old job	
A manual telling you how your new digital camera works	
A history book describing how canals were built	
A presentation about litter and pollution in our towns and cities	

Dear helper
Objective: To distinguish between explanations, reports and recounts.
Task: With your child, go over the boxes showing the key elements of each text type. When they have completed the grid, ask them to explain the reasons for their choices, referring to the grids for support.

NON-FICTION

Name   Date

A load of rubbish!

◾ Cut out the sentences below, which are about how compost is created, and re-order them on another sheet of paper, so that they make sense as an explanation text.

Making the most of waste
This is so that oxygen can help to the waste material start to rot.
It is important that the heap is built in layers of different types of waste, such as grass clippings, vegetable peelings and even crumpled-up newspaper.
But how does this process work?
Next, a rough layer of woody material is arranged to form a base, in such a way that air can circulate.
Finally, after several months, what started as a pile of rubbish will have changed into a brown, crumbly mixture that can be used to feed the soil.
If only one type of waste is used, this slows up the rotting process, and you could end up with a sludgy, smelly mass instead of rich, sweet-smelling compost.
If possible, heaps should be built fairly quickly, in order to create the heat necessary to speed up the transformation.
More and more people are recycling their kitchen and garden waste to make their own compost, which is then used to grow vegetables.
After the heap is made, it may need watering during dry spells, in order to keep the rotting process going, and so that worms can move easily through the mix.
First, a suitable site for the compost bin is selected – usually a place some distance from the house.

Dear helper
Objective: To re-order a series of sentences to create an explanation that makes sense.
Task: Help your child to read through the cut-up sentences, looking for clues that link them together, and bearing in mind the explanation is describing the process in a logical order.

PHOTOCOPIABLE ◾SCHOLASTIC
www.scholastic.co.uk

Name	Date

Researching rubbish

🔲 Make some notes in the boxes below to form the basis of an explanation text about recycling glass. Try to find your information from a variety of sources. Remember you are only making brief notes, not writing the explanation.

🔲 Use your notes to explain something about recycling to your helper. If you have access to the internet, you could use: www.recyclenow.com, www.recycle-more.co.uk, www.recycling-guide.org.uk

Source of information	What it tells me

NON-FICTION

Dear helper
Objective: To do some research as the basis for explaining a process.
Task: Your child may need some help in locating places to find the information. Council leaflets as well as books will be useful. If you do not have internet access, this may be available at your local library. It is advisable to supervise your child if they are using an internet search engine.

Name   Date

NON-FICTION

Crystal clear

■ Using the information you found about recycling glass, write a letter to your local council, explaining ways in which they could help the community to start a scheme of glass recycling. You may wish to use bullet points to separate your information.

_____

_____

_____

Dear _____

_____

_____

_____

_____

_____

_____

_____

_____

_____

_____

_____

_____

Illustrations © Garry Davies.

Dear helper
Objective: To use notes to write a letter of explanation.
Task: The letter should start with a general opening statement before going on to explain some of the ways the scheme could operate. Remind your child they are not writing a persuasive letter, but providing explanations for how such a scheme could work. Ask them to read through the final letter, checking that it fits the criteria for an explanation.

PHOTOCOPIABLE **SCHOLASTIC**
www.scholastic.co.uk

Name	Date

Flushed with success

■ Rewrite this explanation on a separate sheet of paper by:
- ☐ adding link words and phrases where indicated (see list below – you can use a word or phrase more than once)
- ☐ dividing it into paragraphs
- ☐ adding subheadings and numbering – for example, Stage 1; Problems.

Link words and phrases
and   as a result   just in case   or   so that sometimes   this   this means that until   when   which

_____ the handle is pulled, a lever lifts a valve _____ lets the water out of the cistern. _____ flows down a pipe and flushes the toilet. _____, the water level falls _____ the ballcock opens a valve. With the valve open, water pours into the cistern, _____ it fills up again. The ballcock rises _____ the valve is closed. _____ cuts off the water supply _____ the cistern would overflow. _____ something goes wrong, there is an overflow pipe _____ takes the surplus water to an outside pipe so that the floor around the toilet is not flooded. _____ the chain from the lever to the valve comes off or breaks. _____ when you pull the handle nothing happens. Replace the chain – a piece of string will do for a temporary repair. Sometimes the cistern overflows. The ballcock may be leaking. _____ it will not float on the water _____ the valve will not close. Warning – always wash your hands after repairing a toilet!

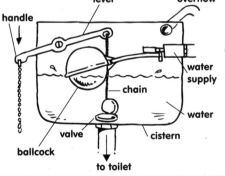
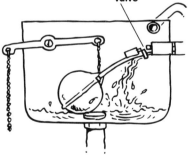
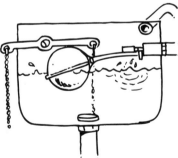

Illustrations © Garry Davies.

Dear helper

Objective: To improve the cohesion of explanations through paragraphing, link phrases, subheadings, numbering and so on.

Task: Read this explanation with your child and discuss which of the linking words and phrases would best fit each gap. Help your child to identify the three stages of the explanation and make these into paragraphs. Finally, discuss suitable headings for each paragraph.

Oddly shaped

An **adjectival phrase** is a group of words that acts like an adjective.

Examples: The clown was **very funny**.
Who is the girl **with the long hair**?

◼ Choose suitable **adjectival phrases** from the list below to fill the gaps in the sentences.

of average height
oddly shaped
strangely disturbing
too cold
too small
very exciting
with the computer
worth reading

1. The book on the table is _____.

2. The classrooms in the new block are _____.

3. The new Super 10 is an _____ car.

4. The suspect is a man _____.

5. That film was _____.

6. James is the boy _____.

7. I found the book _____.

8. The food on the table is _____.

Illustrations © Garry Davies.

Dear helper
Objective: To construct adjectival phrases.
Task: The term *adjectival phrase* may sound difficult, but adjectival phrases are used naturally by all of us. Reassure your child about this, and encourage them to complete the task using common sense – that is, what sounds right.

Word clusters

A **word cluster** is a group of words formed from the same root by adding different **prefixes** and **suffixes**. An example is given below for 'electric'.

CORE SKILLS

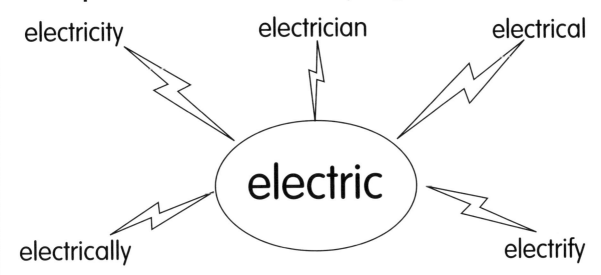

electricity   electrician   electrical

electric

electrically   electrify

■ Make word clusters for these words: **child, employ, love**. Do the first below and then use the back of this sheet.

Extension

■ Choose other words and make word clusters with them.

Dear helper
Objective: To identify root words, words derived from them and spelling patterns.
Task: An awareness of roots, prefixes and suffixes helps with spelling and vocabulary. Remind your child of the following definitions: a root is the basic part of a word to which other parts can be added to change the meaning – a prefix at the beginning, a suffix at the end. Help your child to list all the possible variations of the given root words and to think of other words for which you can make word clusters.

Name   Date

NON-FICTION

Skyliner

■ Read this advertisement and highlight the three things that you find most persuasive.

■ Highlight anything that you think is dishonest.

Travel in the largest airship ever built

Jet powered – London to New York in 8 hours (when wind is favourable)

Safe – unburstable, fireproof   **Good value – prices from £300†**

Flying will be a whole new experience. Instead of a cramped seat, you will have a private cabin*; instead of a seat-back tray, you will dine in a luxury dining room*; instead of a trolley of duty-free goods, you will be able to stroll through a multi-level shopping arcade – and there's more! You can dance in the ballroom, see a show in the theatre, or swim in the glass-bottomed swimming pool which will make you feel that you are swimming through the sky!* You can also stroll on our observation deck‡ to see the fabulous view of New York as we descend to our destination: the airship mooring tower on the world-famous Empire State Building.

*first class only
†economy class single ticket only
‡only when flying at speeds under 50mph, and below 10 000 feet.

Illustrations © Garry Davies.

Dear helper
Objective: To evaluate advertisements for their impact, appeal and honesty.
Task: Read the advertisement with your child and help them to decide which of Skyliner's features are most attractive. Help them to look for anything that is dishonest – even in a small way.

Name   Date

Skyliner complaint

■ Read this letter of complaint. Use a coloured pen to highlight each separate point in the complaint.

■ Using another coloured pen, highlight the connectives.

■ Discuss whether you think the complaint is fair. Remember to look at the original advertisement first.

■ Write a reply from Skyliner Ltd. Would you offer any compensation? if so, what would you offer? Use the back of this sheet.

Dear Sir

I have just got back from my holiday in New York by Skyliner and I have several complaints.

My first complaint is that Skyliner was SLOW! It took 11 hours to get from London to New York, though your advertisement promised eight hours. What is the point of a new type of air transport if it is slower than the types we already have?

Another point is that I did not get a private cabin. I had to sit in an aeroplane-type seat (though I admit there was plenty of space for my legs). Also, I was not allowed in the glass-bottomed swimming pool. This was very disappointing, because I had looked forward to 'swimming through the sky' as you promised in your advertisement.

It was good to be able to sit at a table for a meal, although you did not say in your advertisement that the cost of the meal was extra. Furthermore, the prices were shocking! I had to pay £25 for pizza, sausage and beans!

I was also very disappointed that the observation deck was open only for the last hour of the journey – and then it got very crowded. However, I must say how much I enjoyed flying over New York and ending our journey at the mooring pole on top of the Empire State Building.

Overall, I think Skyliner has some good points, but you need to sort out the problems I have mentioned, and make your advertising more honest. Also, I hope you will be able to offer some compensation for the disappointments I suffered.

Illustrations © Garry Davies.

Dear helper
Objective: To evaluate arguments in a letter of complaint.
Task: Help your child to judge whether the complaints in this letter are fair (your child will have a copy of the Skyliner advertisement). Your child will also need help to draft a reply. Discuss the letter from the company's point of view.

Name   Date

Unsafe at any speed

- Examine this argumentative article about airships by:
  - ☐ numbering the paragraphs;
  - ☐ numbering each point in the argument;
  - ☐ highlighting examples and evidence;
  - ☐ highlighting connectives.

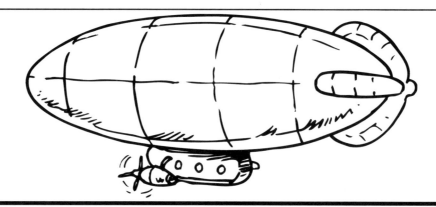

Airship madness

I heard in the news that a new type of passenger airship is being planned. I think this is wrong and should be stopped by the government. The reason is that passenger airships are not safe. We have only to look at the *R101* and the *Hindenburg*, both of which crashed in flames with great loss of life.

Another point is that airships are old fashioned. Even this new design will only be able to reach 300mph – half the speed of a jumbo jet!

However, the manufacturer says that the new airship design will be much safer because it uses helium gas instead of hydrogen, and helium is not inflammable. For this reason, disasters like the *R101* could not take place.

Instead, they say, passengers will have a safe journey with all the luxuries of an ocean liner.

But the manufacturers have not told the whole story. The *R101* crashed because a broken girder tore the fabric. This could still happen, and the airship would crash, even though it would not catch fire. If the safety record of airships was as good as that of aeroplanes, then the new airship might be a good idea, but the fact is that airships are dangerous. They are just too big to control safely.

To sum up, I think there is plenty of evidence to prove that airships are not safe. You can fly on one if you want to, but I'll be going by plane!

Illustrations © Garry Davies.

Dear helper
Objective: To examine how arguments are presented.
Task: Read this article with your child and help them to examine it as explained at the top of the page.

Name	Date

Film trailers

■ Watch a trailer for a film – this may be from a website suggested by your teacher, or a trailer advertising films on a DVD you have at home – then answer the questions below. You may need to watch it more than once.

Title of film _____

What did you like about the trailer, and why?

_____

_____

_____

What did you dislike about the trailer, and why?

_____

_____

_____

How had music been used to persuade you to watch the film?

_____

_____

_____

How had the voice-over been used to persuade you to watch the film?

_____

_____

_____

List any particular words or phrases that were used to try and persuade you.

_____

_____

_____

NON-FICTION

Dear helper
Objective: To identify elements of a film trailer that would persuade a reader to see a film.
Task: If necessary, help your child to select an appropriate film trailer. Ask them to tell you about the reasons for their answers.

Name _____ Date _____

Voice-over

▪ Choose a film you know well, and write a voice-over that could go with a clip from one scene to advertise it. You will need to think about any music or sound effects that you would use as well.

Film title: _____

Briefly describe your chosen clip:

_____

_____

Now write a script for your voice-over, using stage directions to explain how the words should be spoken, and where sound effects and music should happen.

_____

_____

_____

_____

_____

_____

_____

_____

_____

_____

_____

_____

Dear helper
Objective: To write a trailer for a well-known film.
Task: Help your child to choose a suitable clip from a film they know. It should be quite short. Ask them to tell you what they remember about how playscripts are written to help when they write the voice-over. You could watch some film clips from DVDs to help them.

Name   Date

Film poster

🞏 In the space below, design a poster to advertise a film – perhaps one you have already done some work on. Your poster should grab the reader's attention, and use language to persuade them to watch the film. Think about the illustration you will use, and the sizes and colours of the words.

NON-FICTION

Dear helper
Objective: To combine words and images in a persuasive poster.
Task: Talk with your child about the persuasive language used on film posters and in trailers. Encourage them to make their poster simple and bold, making good word choices. Remind them to include the film title, and perhaps the names of some of the actors.

Name   Date

NON-FICTION

Five-point plan

◀ Use this template to write the first draft of a piece of writing in which you present your point of view on a topic. Use the back of this page if required.

Make a point: state your main point and give reasons to support it.

Add another point: give reasons to support it.

Introduce an opposing point: state the opposition's strongest point and give reasons against it.

Discuss the ideas: compare what would happen with your ideas and those of the opposition.

Sum up: state the conclusion you have come to and why.

Dear helper
Objective: To plan the presentation of a point of view.
Task: The most effective way to help your child is to discuss the set topic in detail as this will give your child ideas for writing.

PHOTOCOPIABLE ▮▮SCHOLASTIC
www.scholastic.co.uk

Excel scientific instruments

◼ Read this advertisement and see if you can work out the difficult words from their context (that is, the words around them).

The Excel Company

The Excel Company manufactures and sells a wide range of scientific instruments. Our stethoscopes are so sensitive that a doctor can hear even the faintest sounds within the patient's chest. We also sell a barometer that measures air pressure very accurately - so accurately that some weather forecasters use it. Our theodolite is the first choice of surveyors. It enables them to measure angles and distances precisely, and helps them to plan better roads. We are particularly proud of our chronometers that measure time with an accuracy of plus or minus only a 60th of a second a year. Our electroencephalograph is preferred by many hospitals because of the accuracy with which it measures activity in the brain. If you make a purchase from us, you are sure to be satisfied as all our products come with a one-year warranty.

◼ Complete the glossary below. Then check your definitions using a dictionary.

	Glossary
barometer	
chronometers	
electroencephalograph	
manufactures	
products	
purchase	
stethoscopes	
theodolite	
warranty	

Dear helper
Objective: To figure out the meaning of unknown words from context.
Task: Careful reading of the text will suggest an explanation of the difficult words. Your child should write their best guess in the glossary, then check it against a dictionary.

Big and little

Diminutives are words used to express smallness or affection. They are often (but not always!) formed by adding a suffix.

■ Match each **drawing** to its **diminutive** form by drawing a line to connect them.

Diminutives

statuette

duckling

seedling

kitchenette

piglet

sapling

kitten

booklet

gosling

goose

kitchen

seed

pig

cat

book

duck

statue

tree

Illustrations © Garry Davies.

Extension

■ Use coloured pencils or highlighters to mark suffixes of the same type.

Dear helper
Objective: To understand how diminutives are formed.
Task: Explain any unfamiliar diminutives to your child. Help them to pick the suffixes (word endings) that have been used to form the diminutives. Ask: *Which diminutives are very different from their root words?*

CORE SKILLS

Baby bank

attack	baby	bank	beach	bed	bird
book	bottle	box	boy	bridge	bus
car	cat	chair	check	child	city
class	coat	computer	crowd	day	deep
desk	dream	ear	egg	eye	face
foot	friend	girl	hall	hand	hanger
head	heart	horse	hotel	light	man
master	minder	out	post	room	school

Compound words are formed when two words are joined.
Most compound words are written as one word – **bookcase**.
Some compound words use a hyphen – **twenty-one**.
Some compound words are written as two separate words – **heart attack**.

◼ Cut out the cards and pair them up to find as many known compound words as you can.

◼ Make up new compound words and then make up dictionary definitions for them. Example:

> **baby bank** – a place where you can get cloned babies.

◼ Write all your words and definitions on a separate piece of paper.

Dear helper
Objective: To investigate compound words.
Task: Have fun with your child by combining the word cards in different ways and inventing imaginary definitions.

Dreadful language

English spelling is only partly phonetic. Many spellings are based on meaning – for example, **electricity** is spelled to show its relationship with **electric**. Many spellings are historical – in the Middle Ages, every letter of **knight** was pronounced.

◼ Read and enjoy the poem.

◼ Highlight all the difficult spellings.

I take it you already know
Of tough and bough and cough and dough?
Others may stumble but not you
On hiccough, thorough, tough and through.
Well done! And now you wish perhaps
To learn the less familiar traps.

Beware of heard, a dreadful word,
That looks like beard and sounds like bird;
And dead, it's said like bed not bead –
For goodness' sake don't call it deed!
Watch out for meat and great and threat
(They rhyme with suite and straight and debt).

A moth is not a moth in mother,
Nor both in bother, broth in brother;
And here is not a match for there,
Nor dear and fear for bear and pear,
And then there's dose and rose and lose –
Just look at them – and goose and choose;

And cork and work and card and ward,
And font and front, and word and sword,
And do and go and thwart and cart –
A dreadful language? Man alive,
I'd mastered it when I was five.

Herbert Farjeon

◼ Find other spellings which use the same letter strings. Write them on the back of this sheet.

Poem © Herbert Farjeon; illustrations © Phil Garner.

Dear helper
Objective: To investigate words which have common letter sequences but different pronunciations.
Task: Read and discuss the explanation. Do you know any Europeans who have learned English? What did they find most difficult? Read and enjoy the poem, then investigate the letter sequences by finding matching words.

Make it complex

■ The examples below show some of the ways of forming complex sentences by using different connecting devices. Write your own examples in the empty boxes.

◻ Use a **connective** between two statements to join them together.

Example:	She raided the refrigerator because she was hungry.
Your example:	

◻ Use a **connective** at the beginning of a sentence to join two statements together. Note the comma between the statements.

Example:	Although it was cold, he went out without a coat.
Your example:	

◻ If appropriate, combine the information in statements into a **list** (separate each item except the last with a comma).

Example:	My friend hates maths, PE, English and most other subjects.
Your example:	

◻ Insert a **phrase in apposition** (a phrase of extra information) into a sentence between two commas.

Example:	The doctor, though an elderly man, was very up to date.
Your example:	

◻ Begin a sentence with a **participle** (the **-ing** form of a verb) to join two statements together. Note that a comma is used to mark off the first phrase.

Example:	Climbing the stairs to the attic, I slipped and twisted my ankle.
Your example:	

Illustrations © Ray and Corrine Burrows.

Dear helper
Objective: To use connecting words or phrases to form complex sentences.
Task: Encourage your child to experiment with different ways of connecting points or ideas and to evaluate which links work best.

◖SCHOLASTIC PHOTOCOPIABLE
www.scholastic.co.uk
100 LITERACY HOMEWORK ACTIVITIES · YEAR 4   115

Name   Date

See, saw, stegosaur

A simile is a comparison using **like** or **as**.

■ Read the poem and highlight or underline the similes.

Hello, I'm pleased to meet you,
My back is like a saw,
But don't use me for cutting wood
'Cause I'm a stegosaur.

Now, if you think you're overweight,
Don't worry, I weigh more
(As much as ten 10-ton big trucks)
'Cause I'm a brontosaur.

I'm a pterodactyl –
A bat, a bird? – Not quite!
I'm nothing like a bird at all,
More like a leather kite.

And if you think you're rather sharp
Just look into my jaw:
My teeth are like a row of knives,
'Cause I'm a tyrannosaur.

I'm a tiny mammal,
So small, I'm hard to see
But dinosaurs had better watch out,
'Cause the future belongs to me.

Illustrations © Garry Davies.

■ On the back of this sheet, write about the similes in verses two to four following the pattern below (replace the words in bold when writing about the other verses).

Pattern: The simile in verse **one** compares **the stegosaurus's back** to a **saw**. This is effective because **saw teeth have a similar zig-zag shape**.

Dear helper
Objective: To understand the use of similes in poetry.
Task: Share the reading of the poem with your child. They will need most help when trying to explain why the simile is effective. Discuss: *What is the tiny mammal in the last verse?*

Name	Date

Seeing colours

■ Read this poem, taking care to use the punctuation. Remember to take longer pauses for semi-colons (;) than for commas (,). When you have read it through once, go back and look for the similes, and underline them.

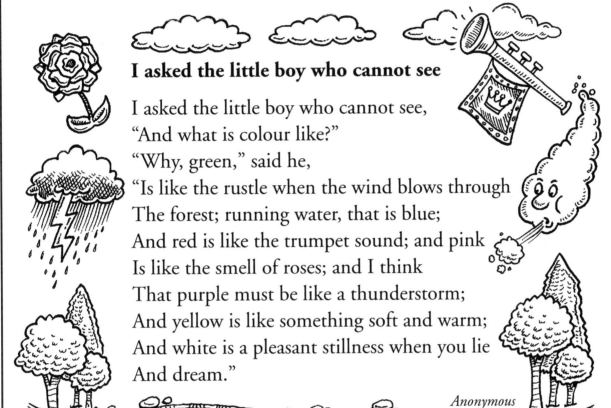

I asked the little boy who cannot see

I asked the little boy who cannot see,
"And what is colour like?"
"Why, green," said he,
"Is like the rustle when the wind blows through
The forest; running water, that is blue;
And red is like the trumpet sound; and pink
Is like the smell of roses; and I think
That purple must be like a thunderstorm;
And yellow is like something soft and warm;
And white is a pleasant stillness when you lie
And dream."

Anonymous

POETRY

■ What images can you create for these colours?

Orange is like _____

Silver is like _____

Brown is like _____

Gold is like _____

Illustrations © Garry Davies.

Dear helper
Objective: To identify and create similes in a poem.
Task: Ask your child to read the poem aloud to you, helping them if they don't use the punctuation correctly. Discuss the similes in the poem before your child attempts to write their own. Share your ideas if they are finding it difficult to create some of their own.

Name	Date

A poem cube

◼ Choose an animal and write four phrases about it using similes – for example, 'Claws as sharp as knives' or 'Skin like the sole of a boot'.

◼ Write your phrases on faces 1, 2, 4 and 5 of the cube and write 'What's in the box?' on face 6 (the lid).

◼ Cut out the net. Write your animal name on the back of face 3.

◼ Glue the net together with your writing inside, leave the lid so that it can open. You have created a mystery poem in a box.

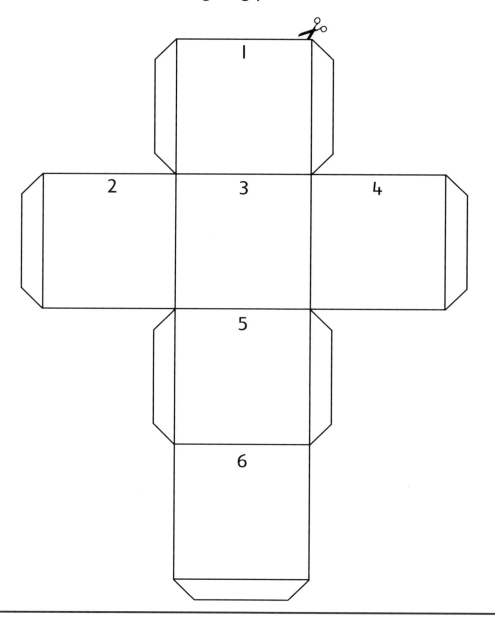

Dear helper
Objective: To write a poem using similes.
Task: Your child should choose an animal they can describe well. Help them to choose distinctive features about it. They may need help to make the cube.

Name

Date

Poem v poem

◼ Use this frame to help you compare and contrast two poems on similar themes. Use the back of this page if you require more space.

	Title:	**Title:**
Subject What does the poet say about the chosen subject? In what ways do the poets treat the subject differently?		
Verse form Is it rhymed verse or free verse? Is there a regular rhythm? Is it set out in verses?		
Vocabulary Jot down any interesting or unusual words and say why they are effective.		
Figures of speech Give an example of a simile or metaphor used by the poet and say why it is effective.		
Preference Which poem did you most enjoy reading and why?		

POETRY

Dear helper
Objective: To compare and contrast poems on similar themes.
Task: Your child will have been given two poems to compare and contrast. Share the reading of the poems with your child, then discuss each of the sections in the table and help your child to complete it.

Mandy's studio

Colons, semi-colons and commas have many uses, but one important use is to make long lists easier to understand.

☐ Colons are used to introduce lists.

☐ Semicolons are used to group items in long lists.

☐ Commas are used to separate individual items in lists.

Example

The museum of Mars contained many interesting exhibits: metal from a spaceship, engine parts and a compass; broken vases, cups, plates and ornaments; and a few fossilised bones of Martians.

Pattern

Introductory clause: item, item, item and item; item, item, item and item; item, item, item and item. (Note: each part of the list can contain fewer or more items.)

◤ Look at the picture of Mandy's art studio. Write a long list describing the three main groups of items in the painting area, the pottery area and the computer area. Use a separate piece of paper.

Illustrations © Garry Davies.

Dear helper

Objective: To identify and use common punctuation marks: colon, semicolon and comma.

Task: Help your child to apply the punctuation pattern to the description of items in the picture.

New word generator

New words are being created all the time to describe new inventions and ideas.

■ Choose a prefix and a word, or a word and a suffix – or even a prefix, word and suffix – to invent a new word.

■ Invent an object to suit the new word and describe it. Example:

new word = biocatalogue   object = catalogue of life forms

Prefix	Word	Suffix
anti-	brain	-able
bio-	catalogue	-a-gram
cyber-	chip	-aholic
desktop-	computer	-athon
e-	consumer	-cred
euro-	environment	-drivel
hyper-	gorilla	-friendly
inter-	kiss	-hostile
net-	language	-modernist
mega-	mail	-ocrat
micro-	market	-ofear
multi-	media	-space
street-	ozone	-speak
super-	star	-struck
techno-	street	-technology
tele-	television	-trendy
web-	video	-zine

■ Add your own prefixes, words and suffixes:

CORE SKILLS

Dear helper

Objective: To invent new words using known words and adding prefixes and suffixes.
Task: This is a fun activity that can be easily shared. If necessary, remind your child of the following definitions: a root is the basic part of a word to which other parts can be added to change the meaning – a prefix at the beginning and a suffix at the end.

Name   Date

Lots of legs

A **couplet** is a pair of lines that rhyme. The rhyme scheme of a poem in couplets is written: **a a**, **b b**, **c c**, and so on.

◾ Complete each of the following **couplets** with the second line, then try to guess which creature it describes.

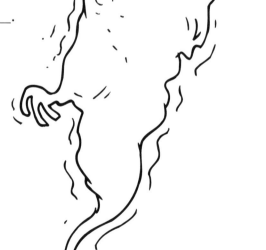

A _ _ _ _
With lots of legs and a funny face
He may drop in from outer _ _ _ _ _.

G _ _ _ _
It dresses in a clean white sheet
And gives us tricks but not much _ _ _ _ _ _.

M _ _ _ _
It's like the one you've had for ages,
But this one's wrapped up in _ _ _ _ _ _ _ _ _.

O _ _ _
A horrible, troll-like, giant creature
Clumsy of fame and coarse of _ _ _ _ _ _ _ _.

T _ _ _ _
A creature of the goblin kind
Which under bridges you may _ _ _ _ _.

U _ _ _ _ _ _ _
This creature is a myth, of course,
But don't get butted by this _ _ _ _ _ _.

Y _ _ _ _
A word like 'snowman' will not do
Without 'abominable' _ _ _.

Illustrations © Garry Davies.

POETRY

Dear helper
Objective: To identify different patterns of rhyme in poetry: couplets.
Task: Help your child to find the rhymes. Note that the number of letters in each missing word is indicated by the small lines.

PHOTOCOPIABLE ◼SCHOLASTIC
www.scholastic.co.uk

Name   Date

The creature of Croglin

Alternate rhyme occurs when alternate lines rhyme with each other. The rhyme scheme of a poem in alternate rhyme is written: **a b a b**, **c d c d** and so on.

◼ Read the poem and see if you can supply the missing rhymes.

Crouching on the moorland bleak

Like a wild beast, is Croglin _ _ _ _:

A lonely place where wild winds _ _ _ _ _ _

Like witches' cats that caterwaul.

Once, on a sultry Summer's night

When Amelia couldn't get to _ _ _ _ _,

She saw outside two points of _ _ _ _ _ _

Not lights – but eyes that seemed to creep

Towards her. She began to weep

And rushed to unlock her bedroom _ _ _ _

But dropped the key! She heard it leap

Inside – glass splintered to the _ _ _ _ _ _ .

She screamed and saw the figure run,

Outlined against the moon's pale _ _ _ _ _ _ .

Her brother chased it with a _ _ _

But it outran him in its fright.

from The Creature of Croglin *by Alex Burrows*

◼ Only part of the poem could be given here. What do you think happens next?

Illustrations © Garry Davies.

POETRY

Dear helper
Objective: To identify different patterns of rhyme in poetry: alternate rhyme.
Task: Help your child to write in the rhymes. Note that the number of letters in each missing word is indicated by the small lines. Help your child with the second task by asking: *What do you think they did next day? Do you think they caught the creature? What kind of creature was it?*

Name   Date

Whale

◼ Read the poem, 'Whale', then write a poem about an animal of your choice by following the prompts.

Whale

Huge
Mighty
Mountainous
Whale
Diving to the deeps
Powerfully
Elegantly
Like a nuclear submarine
I would be sad if you disappeared from the Earth
Whale
Mighty Whale

Prompts	**Your poem**
Write an adjective to describe your animal.	
Write another adjective.	
And another.	
Write the name of your animal.	
Write a verb phrase to describe your animal moving.	
Write an adverb to go with the verb.	
Write another adverb.	
Write a simile comparing your animal to something else.	
Write a line that explains how you feel about your animal.	
Write the name of your animal.	
Write your best adjective for the animal and write the name again.	

Illustrations © Garry Davies.

Dear helper
Objective: To write poetry based on the structure of a poem read.
Task: Help your child to think of a suitable animal and for ideas for each prompt. Write your own poem as well and share it with your child.

Name	Date

Haiku

Haiku (pronounced **high-coo**) is a Japanese form of poetry. It is unrhymed, and short! It has only 17 syllables (arranged in three lines of 5 syllables, 7 syllables and 5 syllables).

◀ Read these haiku poems aloud. Clap and count out the syllables in each line.

◀ Find those that break the rules and see if you can put them right.

Out of film? Try a   _____ syllables

Seventeen syllable verse   _____ syllables

Snapshot – a haiku   _____ syllables

Storm clouds gathering   _____ syllables

The forest sighs in the wind _____ syllables

A screech from an eagle.   _____ syllables

Footsteps on the staircase   _____ syllables

A murmur, a sigh, a knock –   _____ syllables

But no one is there!   _____ syllables

A leaf on the ground,   _____ syllables

Brown and curling –   _____ syllables

Autumn is coming soon.   _____ syllables

Two big floppy ears   _____ syllables

And a bark worse than his bite – _____ syllables

My dog.   _____ syllables

Illustrations © Garry Davies.

POETRY

Dear helper

Objective: To clap out and count syllables in each line of poetry.

Task: Help your child count the syllables in each line of each haiku to find lines where there are too many or too few syllables. Then think of ways to change the line so that it has the right number of syllables, but still keeps to the theme.

From aqua to aquarium

Root word	Modern word	Root word	Modern word
aqua (water)	aquarium	porto (carry)	porter
audio (hear)	audience	rota (wheel)	rotate
centum (hundred)	century	scribo (write)	describe
liber (free)	liberty	unus (one)	unit
navis (ship)	navy	vanus (empty)	vanish
plus (more)	surplus	video (see)	video recorder

Extra words

aquatic	liberal	transport	union
audible	navigate	rotary	vain
cent	plural	manuscript	vision

■ Study the root words and the modern words that have been formed from them.

■ Then, cut out the cards, shuffle them and see if you can match the **root word** with its **modern word**.

Extension

■ Match the extra words to the correct roots.

Dear helper
Objective: To classify words with common roots.
Task: See if your child knows the meaning of the modern English words given. If not, help them use a dictionary to find out.

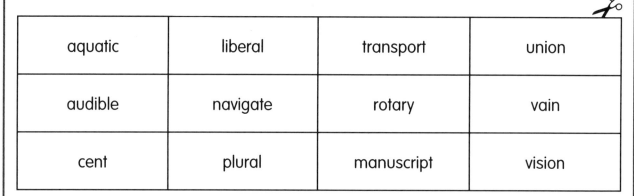

Number prefixes

🔖 Add examples to each section, using a dictionary to help.

Prefix: uni-	**Meaning:** one
unicorn	a mythical horse with **one** horn
Prefix: mono-	**Meaning:** one
monotone	sound with **one** tone
Prefix: bi-	**Meaning:** two
bicycle	a cycle with **two** wheels
Prefix: tri-	**Meaning:** three
triangle	a figure with **three** sides
Prefix: quad-	**Meaning:** four
quadrangle	an open space with **four** sides
Prefix: multi-	**Meaning:** many
multi-storey	a car park with **many** storeys

Extension

🔖 Find words with these number prefixes: **sept-**, **oct-**, **non-**, **cent-**, **mil-**.

Dear helper
Objective: To revise spelling rules for adding prefixes that indicate number.
Task: If necessary, remind your child that a prefix is a letter or group of letters added to the beginning of a word to change its meaning. Watch out for 'bi-' and 'tri-' words. For example, *bitter* has nothing to do with *two* and *trick* has nothing to do with *three*.

Illustrations © Ray and Corrine Burrows.

CORE SKILLS

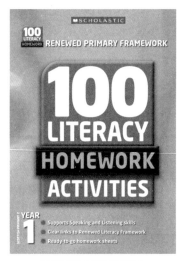

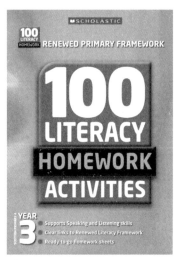